By appointment to
Her Majesty Queen Elizabeth II
Manufacturers of Crispbreads
The Ryvita Co. Ltd. Poole, Dorset

THE

RYVITA

DIET

A range of slimming plans
to suit you & your lifestyle

Jennie Shapter

Cookery Notes

1. Follow either metric or imperial measurements only, for the recipes in this book; they are not interchangeable.
2. All spoon measurements are level unless otherwise stated.
3. Size 3 eggs should be used unless otherwise stated.
4. Cooking times may vary slightly depending on each individual oven. If you have a fan assisted oven adjust temperature and /or timing according to the manufacturer's instructions.
5. Place dishes in the centre of the oven unless otherwise stated.

Published exclusively for
The Ryvita Company Limited,
by Victor Steeden Associates Limited,
1, Oakmead, Seven Hills Road, Cobham, Surrey KT11 1EU.

ISBN 0 9521084 0 2 – Hardback
ISBN 0 9521084 1 0 – Paperback

Design : Victor Steeden
Editor : Jennie Shapter
Design & Typesetting : Simon Steeden
Photography : Victor Steeden
Jerry Tubby (cover)
Adrian Bradley (pages 8-10)
Home Economist : Jennie Shapter
Stylist : Maria Kelly
Illustrations : Philip Kerrey

Acknowledgements:
Special thanks to the YMCA London Branch and Slimmer Magazine for providing the Y Plan exercises

Contents

Zip into Shape

Bringing together Ryvita's know-how from 60 years of helping slimmers.

Ryvita has over sixty years experience in helping countless slimmers and learning from them. Enjoyable and tasty in itself, Ryvita also provides an excellent complement to so many other 'right kinds' of food. One of the earliest catch phrases was "Makes you fit and keeps you slim" and there are thousands of case-histories from users who testify to its value this way.

That's why the Ryvita company had this book specially written. It incorporates all the knowledge and practical experience we have gained and embodies the sound principles of diet which have been the fount of Ryvita's success over the years.

But make no mistake, it's emphatically not simply a list of 'things on Ryvita'. There is an almost infinite variety of foods, with menus for all times of day and all occasions, including meals at work, with the rest of the family, even when entertaining. Nowadays, there's an abundance of appetising, highly nutritious but sometimes downright rich food, all too readily available. Add the pressures of modern life that can make it hard to choose 'what's best' in preference to 'what's quickest' and it's not surprising that most of us could benefit from losing at least some weight.

Obviously, there are many reasons for wanting to do something about your diet, including general health. But most of us would simply like to look a little sleeker, with a few less bulges and a little more comfort in clothes that used to fit perfectly. And, of course, once you do lose that excess weight you simply _feel_ so much better.

Zipping into shape

Fortunately, getting slimmer and fitter needn't be hard work, boring, complicated, monotonous or anti-social. Whether you're making a major effort to put things right or simply looking for a better permanent balance in what you eat and the way you live.

The Ryvita diets have a series of varied and interesting recipes that build into plans to suit all kinds of lifestyles – or which can be selected just because you fancy them.

This attractively-illustrated book also has explanations of healthy eating generally, charts of ideal weight ranges, hints on exercise, and a whole list of suggestions for lower calorie or healthier alternatives to foods you love but which don't love you. All in straightforward terms, with no fussy, faddy, 'magic' foods or systems.

It's a mouthwateringly enjoyable read as any good cook-book should be ... and you're bound to find a host of ideas that are right as well as good for you.

This is an example of a typical day's allowance of 1200 calories.

5

How Much Should You Weigh?

Energy is required for us to live, from breathing right through to strenuous exercise. Obviously the amount needed is variable according to each persons' daily activities. If you eat or drink foods which provide more energy than you require, the excess will be converted into body fat.

It is difficult to determine your ideal weight as frame sizes vary from person to person within each height band. There is no point trying to model yourself on someone with a totally different body frame to yours. A glance in the mirror often answers the question – do I need to lose weight?

The charts below will enable you to find the weight range for your height, within which you should aim to stay.

To use the charts:
● Weigh yourself without clothes. If this is not possible, remove shoes and any outdoor garments. Allow 2kg (4-5lb) for indoor clothes.
● Measure your height without any shoes on.
● Refer to either the male or female chart. Run a line horizontally from your height and vertically from your weight. Where these two lines cross will show if you are overweight or not.

If you need to lose weight follow one of the Zip into Shape Diets provided in this book. With all diets, it is important to consult your Doctor before starting, if you are not in good general health. Do not diet whilst pregnant, unless medically advised to.

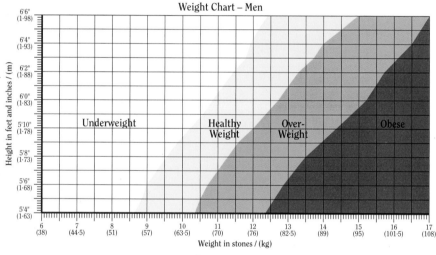

Weight Chart – Men

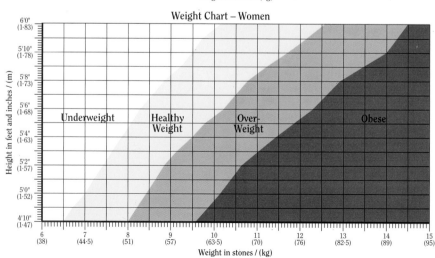

Weight Chart – Women

How to Diet and Stay Healthy

HOW TO DIET & STAY HEALTHY

A daily calorie requirement for the average woman is around 2100 calories and for the average man 2500-2900 calories depending on the amount of physical work or exercise. To lose weight you need to reduce the amount of calories eaten. It is better to lose weight slowly, around 0.5-1kg (1-2lb) per week, than to try a crash diet which will leave you hungry, and in the long term is less likely to be successful.
The slimming diets in this book allow 1200 calories a day for a woman and 1500 calories a day for a man. This will give a 0.5-1kg (1-2lb) weight loss per week, (may be slightly more to begin with or if you have a lot of weight to lose). If you do have a lot of weight to lose then you may find that you can increase your calorie allowance by 200 calories per day and still lose weight. Once you have reached your ideal weight it is important to remember that your change of eating pattern is for life, otherwise you may drift back into bad eating habits and gain weight.

HEALTHY EATING & A BALANCED DIET

By following the Diet for Life on pages 52-71 you will have a core of recipes which will help to ensure you eat a sensible healthy diet, i.e. high in dietary fibre, low in fat and salt and with a good proportion of energy being provided by starchy carbohydrates.
The recipes in this section and the food listed in the Calories, Fat and Fibre Guide on pages 90-94 include fat and fibre values as well as calorie values, to help you select the right types of foods.
Over the last few years various medical committees have published reports on how your health is linked to your diet. They all recommend similar healthier eating patterns. Here are some of the recommendations and how to achieve them.

FAT

In the UK, we tend to eat too much fat, up to nearly 40% of our total calorie intake. You should try to reach a fat consumption of 35% and eventually 30%. A 35% fat intake allows around 97-117g (3½-4oz) fat a day, depending on your calorie intake, whilst a 30% fat intake allows around 84g (3oz) for a woman eating 2100 calories and 100g (3½oz) for a man eating 2500 calories.
Whilst reducing the amount of fat in your diet, cut down on saturated fats, found in such foods as butter, full fat cheese or milk,

meat fat, pastry and chocolate. Saturated fats increase blood cholesterol levels and can lead to heart disease. No more than one third of your fat intake should be hard saturated fat. Polyunsaturated fats are mainly found in foods from vegetable sources, such as liquid oils from plant seeds, such as sunflower oil, and in solid form from nuts and grains.
To cut down on fat intake remove visible fat from meat and choose lower fat types like chicken or turkey, use skimmed or semi-skimmed milk and lower fat cheeses. Replace cream with yogurt. Low fat spreads have half or even less than half the calories of margarine and butter.

DIETARY FIBRE & CARBOHYDRATES

High fibre foods help to keep the digestive system functioning properly and along with starch carbohydrates are more filling than other foods. High fibre foods take longer to chew, and are more satisfying, reducing hunger pangs.
The current average daily intake is around 20g (¾oz), whilst 30g (1oz) is actually the recommended level.
Fruit and vegetables provide useful amounts of dietary fibre. Include the skins of vegetables such as potatoes and fruits such as apples and pears. Eat pulses, nuts, whole-grain cereals, brown rice, pasta and rye or wholemeal based crispbreads and breads.

REDUCING SALT

There is a link in certain groups of people between excessive salt intake and high blood pressure. Most people eat more salt than they need, around 8-12 grams a day. This should be reduced to 5-7 grams.
Try to avoid adding lots of salt during cooking, or sprinkling over food at the table. Add herbs and spices for flavouring instead. Be aware of the high levels of salt found in many packaged foods.

REDUCING SUGAR

The average sugar consumption per person is around 45kg (100lb) a year. Sugar provides calories and energy to the diet, but if not needed immediately by the body, it will be converted to fat and so encourage weight gain. It is suggested that sugar intake should be reduced to 20kg (44lb) per person per year. To try and cut down, do not add sugar to drinks and reduce amount added in cooking. Replace sticky puddings with fresh fruit. Look out for hidden sugar in manufactured foods including many savoury foods.

Exercises

Dieting is an important start to achieving a new fitter, sleeker physique, but it is only part of the story. You also need to combine it with some exercise. As well as helping to lose weight, by burning extra calories, exercise will tone flabby muscles, to give you a leaner look and a firm more defined body.

While exercising wear comfortable clothing, preferably cotton; shoes with all round support and cushioning and work on a soft surface.

Always start gently and gradually build up to more vigorous activities. Breathe easily throughout. Stop immediately if you feel pain and if it persists seek medical advice.

THE WARM UP

A warm up should include three types of exercise: mobility for the joints; pulse raising to warm the muscles and stretching to lengthen the muscles.

The Pelvic Tilt

A basic exercise which is fundamental to good technique.
● Stand with feet shoulder width apart and knees very slightly bent.
● Tilt pelvis forward by pulling in tummy muscles and slightly rounding lower back, as you tuck buttocks under and feel lower back lengthen. Feel tummy muscles working.

Mobility and Pulse Raising Exercises

1. Full Arm Circles
● Stand with feet shoulder width apart, arms extended at either side and a good pelvic tilt.
● Bend knees and circle arms down across in front of body. As arms begin to rise, extend legs and rise up onto toes as arms reach above head. Continue moving arms to complete circle while lowering heels back to floor.
● Repeat slowly 8 times.

2. Shoulder Circles
● Stand with feet shoulder width apart and toes pointing forward with a good pelvic tilt.
● Keep hips facing forwards and circle right shoulder taking it forwards and up, round and down, making as large an imaginary circle as possible with top of shoulder.
● Do once more then repeat using other shoulder.

3. Heel, Toe and Knee Lift
● Stand with weight on left leg, knees slightly bent and right foot pointed on the floor.
● Flex and point right foot in a heel toe action then lift and lower right knee taking it up and slightly across the body towards the opposite side of the chest. At the same time bend and straighten the opposite arm pulling the elbow towards the knee.
● Repeat exercise 8 times with each leg.

4. Twists
● Stand with feet hip width apart, knees bent and over toes and a good pelvic tilt.
● Bend arms at elbow and bring forearms into rest one on top of other at chest level. With control, twist body from waist to right. Hold for a second and repeat to the right. Return to centre and repeat to left.

Return to beginning of Mobility and Pulse Raising Sequence and repeat, this time putting more energy into the performance.

Stretching

1. Inner Thigh Stretching

- Stand with feet wide apart and toes pointing slightly outwards.
- Bend left knee in line with left foot, then slide right leg sideways until you feel a stretch in your inner thigh.
- Hold for 8 seconds then repeat on other side.

2. Hamstring Stretch

- Stand with legs hip width apart and feet parallel, left leg slightly bent and hands on thigh for support.
- Keeping shoulders pulled back to keep back straight, bend forwards from hips until you feel a stretch in back of right leg.
- Hold for 8 seconds then repeat on other side.

3. Quad Stretch

- Face a wall or chair for support. Transfer weight to left leg, bend knee slightly and tuck bottom under as for pelvic tilt.
- Bring right heel back and up towards buttocks and, using right hand to assist, lift heel toward buttock until you feel stretch down front of thigh.
- Hold for 8 seconds, then repeat using other leg.

TONING EXERCISES

1. Tummy Toner

- Lie on back, legs bent up over trunk, knees over navel, arms extended towards shins.
- Keeping small of back in contact with floor, pull tummy in flat. Hold it there and reach for your toes by curling your head and shoulders off the floor. Relax.
- Repeat 6 times.

2. Waist Worker

- Lie on back with legs bent up over trunk. Place both arms to right side of right thigh.
- Pulling tummy in flat and holding it, slowly reach arms to the right of legs by curling head and shoulders.
- Repeat 6 times.

3. Buttock Burner

- Lie on back with legs and feet flat on floor. Keeping back straight, raise hips slightly off floor to make a straight line from ribs to knees.
- Keeping hips and back still, bend one leg into chest, then extend it up towards ceiling. Holding tummy tight to stabilise back, lower leg keeping it straight until foot is about 30 cm (12 in) off the floor.
- Bend leg and place foot on floor as for start position. Repeat with other leg.
- Repeat 4 times.

4. Arm Improver

- Stand with feet hip width apart. Raise arms above head, straight, brushing ears with upper arms, palms facing inward.
- Keeping arms straight, lower them by taking them out, palms up, down and then backwards, squeezing the backs of your hands and shoulder blades towards each other.
- Raise arms up above head again to start position. Repeat 6 times, rest and repeat.

5. Hip Toner

- Stand side on to a wall or chair for support with outside leg to the side and foot resting on the floor.
- Keeping hips level and facing front, gently raise outside leg to side, then lower.
- Repeat 6 times, rest and repeat. Turn round and repeat exercise with other leg.

6. Thigh Toner

- Sit with one leg slightly bent, foot flat on floor, back straight and leaning back on your hands. Straighten other leg out in front, holding it slightly off the floor.
- Keeping tummy muscles tight to hold back still, gently raise straight leg up to height of knee of bent leg. Lower to start position.
- Repeat 6 times, rest and repeat. Change legs and repeat exercise.

THE COOL DOWN

This is now a time to slow down, relax and feel comfortable.

1. Front Quad Stretch

- Lie on front with forehead resting on hands. Tuck bottom under and tilt pelvis up towards nose. Bend one leg up towards bottom. Point toe and take hold of ankle. Re-tilt pelvis. Gently ease heel in towards bottom until you feel a stretch.
- Hold for 8 seconds. Repeat with other leg.

2. Shoulder Stretch

- Kneel with buttocks on heels and hands on floor in front with thumbs close together. Extend arms in front of you and keep chest resting on thighs.
- Keeping chest low, slide hands and hips forwards, raising buttocks up off heels until hips are directly above knees.
- Keeping hips high, push chest down towards knees until you feel stretch in shoulders. Hold for 8 seconds.

3. Buttock Stretch

- Leaning back on hands for support, sit with left leg bent, foot flat on floor and other leg bent with ankle resting on left knee.
- Using arms to assist movement, sit up so that you take tummy and chest towards thighs until you feel a stretch in buttocks of right leg.
- Hold for 16 seconds, trying to gently increase the stretch. Repeat with other leg.

4. Hamstring Stretch

- Sit with legs slightly bent out in front of you. Lean towards thighs and use hands on floor for slight support.
- Keeping trunk still and your back as straight as possible, gently extend one leg and flex foot until you feel stretch down back of thigh.
- Hold for 16 seconds, trying to relax and gently increase the stretch. Repeat with other leg.

How Ryvita can help

Ryvita can play an important role as part of your everyday diet. Ryvita is an ideal substitute for bread as slice for slice Ryvita contains only 25 calories or 33 for sesame, instead of around 80 calories for bread. Ryvita's composition follows recommended health guidelines in that it is low in fat and high in fibre. Ryvita is made from ground wholemeal rye with just a tiny amount of salt added (less than 1%).

There is no added fat, the small amount present is from the germ of the rye. Ryvita is rich in fibre which helps to satisfy the appetite and keep the digestive system in good working order.

Rye is a natural source of vitamin B_1, important to the digestion. Rye also contains pentosans. These gelatinise and swell in the stomach, and so slow down digestion and absorption, which in turn helps to stave off hunger pangs.

Ryvita does not contain any added sugar, which can contribute to tooth decay and possible weight gain.

Zip into Shape Diets

A selection of diets with Ryvita which will
help to shape the rest of your life.

Calorie counting is just part of an overall eating pattern. Often a diet is seen as just a short period of deprivation to lose a few pounds or kilos, followed by a return to your original diet. Fast 'crash' diets may give a short term success, but sooner or later the weight will gradually creep back on. Without a change in eating habits you will be on a continuous cycle of on/off eating.

It is important to consider dieting not just as a temporary idea, but as a gradual change to a new way of eating; with the aim of losing weight slowly and staying at the new lower weight.

The need to lose weight is due to an incorrect diet in the first instance. For your dieting to be a success, a new way of eating which leaves you feeling satisfied but slimmer, is necessary.

The Ryvita Zip into Shape Diets have been written to help you do just that. First of all there is a choice of two weight loss diets to follow, then there is a section of recipes designed to help you eat healthily after reaching your target weight.

The choice of weight loss diets are either a rigid Day by Day Diet plan or a more flexible Mix and Match Diet. Whether you are male or female, at work or in the home, one of these diets is sure to suit.

The Day by Day Diet is ideal for people who want all the decision making taken out of their diet. It provides a list of foods to eat at every mealtime, for 14 days. Just repeat to complete a four week diet.

Some people prefer the flexibility of selecting their own meals, and this can be achieved by following the Mix and Match Diet.

If you are at work during the day you can select recipes which may easily be prepared in advance and taken in a plastic container. There is also a choice of soup, which can easily be transported in a flask, if you prefer something hot on a cold day. Snacks and lunches or light meals in these two diet sections which can be transported have been marked with an asterisk thus *.

When preparing food in advance, just

Zip into Shape Diets

remember the following simple guidelines. Keep toppings separate from crispbreads and combine when required. Dress salads and cut apples or pears just before eating.

The recipes have been chosen to ensure most tastes are catered for, whether you are a vegetarian, non-meat eater or like to eat a completely mixed diet including red meats. Unlike many low calorie recipes, which can often be bland, these include lots of interesting flavourings using herbs, spices, marinades and sauces.

Both diets allow a daily intake of 1200 calories which includes 280 ml (½ pt) of skimmed milk per day for tea and coffee. If you prefer semi-skimmed milk then you may have 225 ml (8 floz) to compensate for the slightly higher calorie content.

These two diets are based on a daily calorie intake of 1200 calories so that you lose weight steadily. Depending upon how much weight you need to lose, your weight loss will vary. Assuming you are following a four week diet plan, you can expect to lose at least 6lb/2·5kg and up to 10lb/4·5kg or more.

The Mix and Match Diet follows the increasingly popular method of dieting which allows you five small meals per day. This method of eating, often referred to as grazing, is encouraged by experts as scientific evidence suggests extra fat burning occurs when you eat a little and often. Your five meals can be taken as breakfast, snack, lunch, main meal and dessert, but providing you select 1100 calories a day you have the beauty of being able to choose from whichever category you wish. Make sure you select a good cross section of foods each day and only one dessert.

All the recipes are calorie counted per serving and the number of servings are also indicated.

Whichever diet you are following make sure you eat and drink everything recommended in the diet. Also maintain a good fluid intake.

Unlimited amounts of black tea, coffee, or with milk from your allowance, water and calorie free drinks are allowed. No sugar is allowed in tea or coffee.

If you are a man following these diets then it is important to increase your calorie intake to 1500 per day. If you are following the Day by Day Diet select a 100 calorie snack from pages 32-39; increase your daily milk allowance to 420ml (¾ pt) of skimmed milk and choose from 100g (4oz) cooked brown or white rice; 110g (4oz) cooked whole wheat or white pasta or 170g (6oz) jacket or mashed potato each day. You can follow the same additions for the Mix and Match Diet, or select meals with higher calorie values up to 1400 calories, to leave 100 calories for your milk allowance.

Once you have reached your target weight follow the Diet for Life section, these recipes include foods which are higher in fibre and lower in fat and sugar. It is generally recognised that most of us eat too much fat and sugar and insufficient fibre. It is important to include lots of fresh fruit and vegetables as well as plenty of cereals and whole grain foods such as wholemeal pasta and brown rice in your diet. Ryvita can help you maintain your new eating plan, for it is a good source of dietary fibre, low in fat and sugar.

The recipes in this section reflect the correct types of food to eat and help to show you new ways of cooking foods using less fat and sugar. It includes lower calorie family favourites as well as new ideas.

So with all this information at your fingertips, there's no excuse, just turn the page and start your new diet.

Day by Day Diet

Successful slimming is all too often seen as a penance. It is easy to make excuses as to why you don't have time to go on a diet. I'll start tomorrow, is an all too frequent phrase.

With this diet all the hard work of calorie counting, and what to eat, when, has been done for you.

It gives 14 days of menus. To complete a 28 day diet, just go back to day one and repeat the diet.

Each day you have a breakfast, snack, lunch, main meal and dessert. If you prefer your main meal in the middle of the day then merely swap it with the lunch suggestion.

Most of the recipes can be found on pages 20-51. The remaining few are written within each day's menu.

If after 14 days you wish to select your own menus switch to the mix and match diet on page 18.

In addition to your day by day diet you are allowed 280 ml (½ pt) skimmed milk for use in tea and coffee.

For those who wish to follow this diet whilst working, the snacks and lunches marked * can be carried to work. Assuming a Monday to Friday working week, start Day 1 on a Monday.

Day 1

Breakfast: 1 Ryvita Original crispbread with 1 tsp low fat spread and 1 size 3 egg, boiled.
1 Ryvita Sesame crispbread spread with 2 tsp reduced sugar marmalade.

Snack: Easy Carrot Soup* (see page 34)

Lunch: Crab Snackers* (see page 25)

Main Meal: Warm Chinese Salad (see page 45)

Dessert: Banana Special (see page 41)

Day 2

Breakfast: Brunch Kebabs (see page 20)

Snack: 25g (1oz) low fat liver pâté served with 1 grated carrot, 1 stick celery, 1 spring onion, 2 cherry tomatoes and 1 Ryvita Oat Bran crispbread.*

Lunch: Tuna Pasta Salad* (see page 29)

Main Meal: Turkey and Cider Hot Pot (see page 48)

Dessert: Apple and Kiwi Sorbet (see page 35)

Day 3

Breakfast: Cheesy Beans (see page 22)

Snack: Prawn and Cucumber Dip* (see page 36)

Lunch: Slice 1 large onion and fry in 1 tbsp sunflower oil. Add 300 ml (½ pt) beef stock and cook for 10 minutes. Season. Serve soup topped with 1 tbsp grated mature Cheddar cheese. Serve with 2 Ryvita Dark Rye crispbreads, topped with 25g (1oz) ham.*

Main Meal: Beef and Vegetable Pie (see page 44)

Dessert: Apricot Rice Pots (see page 43)

Day 4

Breakfast: Demon Kidneys (see page 30)

Snack: Gazpacho* (see page 38)

Lunch: Rice Salad* (see page 21)

Main Meal: Pork Fillet with Oranges (see page 48)

Dessert: Vanilla Cloud (see page 37)

Day 5

Breakfast: Fruity Porridge (see page 26)

Snack: Tomato and Onion Salad* (see page 32)

Lunch: Piquant Chicken Bites* (see page 27)

Main Meal: Tuna Macaroni Bake (see page 50)

Dessert: Mix 1 sliced orange and 75g (3oz) strawberries together. Sprinkle with 2 tsp flaked almonds and serve with 1 tbsp strained Greek style yogurt.

Day 6

Breakfast: 3 tomatoes, halved and grilled; served with 2 Ryvita Oat Bran crispbreads spread with 2 tsp low fat spread.
150 ml (5 floz) glass unsweetened orange juice.
50g (2oz) grapes.

Snack: Devilled Mushrooms (see page 34)

Lunch: Baked Cheese Specials (see page 31)

Main Meal: Seafood Pasta (see page 44)

Dessert: Mini Meringue Nests (see page 37)

Day 7

Breakfast: Breakfast Mushrooms (see page 30)

Snack: Serve 20g (¾oz) sliced brie on 1 Ryvita Dark Rye crispbread with 1 tsp pickle.*

Lunch: Egg Florentine Style (see page 21)

Main Meal: Beef Stir Fry (see page 47)

Dessert: Fresh Fruit Dip (see page 39)

Day 8

Breakfast: Grapefruit Compote (see page 20)

Snack: Fruit and Nut Crunch* (see page 38)

Lunch: 110g (4oz) mixed bean salad on a bed of shredded Chinese leaves. Serve with 25g (1oz) sliced chicken and 1 Ryvita Original crispbread.*

Main Meal: Broccoli Cheese Flan (see page 51)

Dessert: Rhubarb Flummery (see page 33)

Day 9

Breakfast: Savoury Breakfast Omelette (see page 28)

Snack: Chocolate and Strawberry Crispbread* (see page 36)

Lunch: Trout Platter* (see page 25)

Main Meal: Chicken Korma (see page 46)

Dessert: Peel and slice 1 pear and poach in 150 ml (¼ pt) dry cider with 2 cloves, a stick of cinnamon and 1 tsp muscovado sugar, until tender. Chill before serving.

Day 10

Breakfast: Early Riser (see page 22)

Snack: Stuffed Pears* (see page 32)

Lunch: Parma Ham Crispbreads* (see page 23)

Main Meal: Lamb Medley (see page 47)

Dessert: Cheesy Fruit Cups (see page 43)

Day 11

Breakfast: 25g (1oz) muesli with milk from daily allowance.
125g (4·4oz) pot diet fruit yogurt mixed with 1 small sliced banana.

Snack: Cheese Toppers* (see page 40)

Lunch: Hearty Vegetable Soup* (see page 27)

Main Meal: Italian Fish Casserole (see page 46)

Dessert: Mixed Fruit Terrine (see page 33)

Day 12

Breakfast: Hawaiian Crispbreads (see page 24)

Snack: 50g (2oz) tuna in brine, drained, mixed with 1 tbsp skimmed milk quark and 1 chopped spring onion. Serve on a lettuce leaf with cress. Serve with 1 Ryvita Original crispbread.*

Lunch: Tabbouleh* (see page 31)

Main Meal: Spicy Chicken Kebabs (see page 49)

Dessert: Orange Granita (see page 39)

Day 13

Breakfast: Fruit and Yogurt Swirl (see page 24)

Snack: Italian Melts (see page 42)

Lunch: 2 grilled fish fingers served with lettuce leaves, cucumber and 50g (2oz) reduced calorie coleslaw. 2 Ryvita Oat Bran crispbreads.

Main Meal: Gammon and Pineapple Pizza (see page 45)

Dessert: Summer Compote (see page 35)

Day 14

Breakfast: Speedy Starter (see page 26)

Snack: Cheese and Tomato Toasties (see page 40)

Lunch: Turkey Stir Fry (see page 23)

Main Meal: Filo Fish Pie (see page 49)

Dessert: Heat 150 ml (¼ pt) semi-skimmed milk with 2 tsp sugar and 1 heaped tsp coffee granules until just warm to the finger. Stir in ½ tsp rennet and pour into a serving dish. Leave in a warm place for 1 hour, to set. Chill and serve dusted with grated nutmeg.

Mix and Match Diet

This diet is ideal for anyone with a busy lifestyle. Whether you are out at work or looking after a family at home, life is often hectic and it is impossible to follow a regimented diet plan.

This diet has total flexibility which can be organised to suit your own particular needs. Each day you have five meals plus 280 ml (½ pt) skimmed milk for use in tea and coffee.

Select 1 Breakfast; 1 Light Meal; 1 Snack; 1 Dessert and 1 Main Meal.

Pages 20-51 are full of calorie counted recipes for all of these meals. All you have to do is select 5 meals per day and add up the calories to give 1100 per day. Each double page has a calorie flash on the corner for easy reference.

For example:

Breakfast: Grapefruit Compote, page 20, 200 calories
Light Meal: Egg Florentine Style, page 21, 200 calories
Snack: Tomato and Onion Salad, page 32, 100 calories
Dessert: Apricot Rice Pot, page 43, 200 calories
Main Meal: Seafood Pasta, page 44, 400 calories

If you prefer you can replace your dessert with a snack. You can eat your selected meal whenever you choose, but avoid saving everything for the evening.

It is better to eat a little and often.

For those who wish to follow this diet whilst working, the snacks and lunches marked * can be carried to work.

Mix and Match Diet Index

Brunch Kebabs

Serves 1

1 beef chipolata sausage
1 rasher streaky bacon
4 button mushrooms
2 cherry tomatoes, halved
1 tsp sunflower oil
2 Ryvita Dark Rye crispbreads

1. Twist sausage in the centre to make two small sausages and cut in half. Cut bacon in half and roll up.

2. Thread sausages, mushrooms and bacon rolls onto two small skewers.

3. Brush mushrooms and sausage with oil and cook under a preheated grill for 8-10 minutes, turning 2-3 times. Add tomatoes for last 2 minutes.

4. Serve with Ryvita Dark Rye crispbreads.

Grapefruit Compote

Serves 1

2 dried figs
3 dried apricots
150 ml (¼ pt) apple juice
1 pink grapefruit, peeled, with pith removed and segmented
2 dessert plums, stoned and sliced

1. Place the figs, apricots and apple juice in a pan and bring to the boil. Cover and simmer for 15 minutes.

2. Transfer to a bowl, cover and leave to cool.

3. Lightly stir in the grapefruit segments and plums. Cover and chill, overnight if wished.

Egg Florentine Style

Serves 1

75g (3oz) fresh spinach, roughly chopped, or frozen
salt and freshly ground black pepper
1 egg
¼ tsp grated nutmeg
25g (1oz) ricotta cheese
2 tsp grated Parmesan cheese
1 Ryvita Original crispbread

1. Wash fresh spinach and place in a saucepan with a little salt and just the water that clings to the leaves. Cook for 5-8 minutes until tender. Drain well. Cook frozen spinach according to pack instructions.

2. Meanwhile poach egg. Mix spinach with nutmeg, pepper and ricotta cheese. Place in a heat-proof dish with the egg on top.

3. Sprinkle with Parmesan cheese. Place under a preheated grill to brown, if wished. Serve with a Ryvita Original crispbread.

Rice Salad*

Serves 1

25g (1oz) long grain rice
2 tbsp oil free French dressing
1 tbsp fresh chopped tarragon or parsley
4 radishes, sliced
5 cm (2 in) piece cucumber, chopped
1 tbsp sweetcorn kernels
50g (2oz) bean-sprouts
1 tomato, chopped
2 spring onions, chopped
1 Ryvita Dark Rye crispbread

1. Cook the rice in boiling salted water for about 12 minutes, until just tender. Drain and rinse.

2. Mix the oil free French dressing and tarragon together and pour over the rice. Leave until cold.

3. Mix radishes, cucumber, sweetcorn, bean-sprouts, tomato and spring onions together. Add to rice and toss together. Serve with Ryvita Dark Rye crispbread.

Cheesy Beans

Serves 1

*110g (4oz) low calorie baked beans in
tomato sauce*
1 tsp French mustard
25g (1oz) lean ham, cut into strips
1 spring onion, chopped
2 Ryvita Original crispbreads
1 tbsp grated Parmesan cheese

1. Place the beans in a small pan. Mix in the
mustard, ham and spring onion and heat
gently until hot.

2. Meanwhile sprinkle Ryvita Original
crispbreads with Parmesan cheese and place
under a preheated grill to brown.

3. Serve beans on cheese topped crispbreads.

Early Riser

Serves 1

1 egg, lightly beaten
1 tbsp skimmed milk
salt and freshly ground black pepper
1 tsp butter
25g (1oz) button mushrooms, sliced
150 ml (¼ pt) tomato juice
dash Tabasco sauce
ice cubes and celery leaves to serve
1 tsp fresh chopped dill
2 Ryvita Dark Rye crispbreads

1. Lightly beat the egg, milk and seasoning
together. Place the butter in a small non-
stick pan and heat gently to melt. Add the
mushrooms and cook for 2 minutes.

2. Add the egg mix and cook over a medium
heat, stirring occasionally, until eggs begin
to coagulate.

3. Meanwhile mix tomato juice and Tabasco
together. Place in a glass, top up with ice
cubes and garnish with celery.

4. Stir dill into egg and serve on top of
Ryvita Dark Rye crispbreads. Serve
with tomato juice.

200 CALORIES per serving

Turkey Stir Fry

Serves 1

2 tsp sesame oil
1 clove garlic, crushed
1 tsp fresh ginger root, grated
25g (1oz) mangetout
½ red pepper, cut into matchstick strips
25g (1oz) button mushrooms, sliced
40g (1½oz) cooked turkey, cut into thin strips
1 spring onion, cut into 2·5 cm (½ in) lengths
1 tbsp soy sauce
salt and freshly ground black pepper

1. Heat the oil in a non-stick wok or frying pan. Add the garlic, ginger, mangetout, pepper and mushrooms and stir fry for 2-3 minutes.

2. Add the turkey and spring onions and cook for a further 1-2 minutes.

3. Stir in the soy sauce, season to taste and serve.

Parma Ham Crispbreads*

Serves 1

1 tbsp strained Greek style yogurt
¼ red onion, finely chopped
2 Ryvita Oat Bran crispbreads
salad leaves
25g (1oz) thinly sliced Parma ham, torn into strips
2 cherry tomatoes, cut into wedges
freshly ground black pepper
100g (4oz) Ogen or Charentais melon, sliced

1. Mix yogurt and onion together. Spread over Ryvita Oat Bran crispbreads.

2. Arrange salad leaves, Parma ham and tomatoes on top and season with freshly ground pepper.

3. Serve with slices of melon.

Fruit and Yogurt Swirl

Serves 1

3 tbsp low fat natural yogurt
2 tbsp smatana
1 tbsp muscovado sugar
¼ tsp ground cinnamon
1 apple
1 peach or pear, cut into segments
1 kiwi

1. Mix yogurt and smatana together and place in a small bowl. Mix sugar and cinnamon together and sprinkle over.

2. Core apple and cut into eight. Stone peach or core pear and cut into bite size pieces. Peel and slice kiwi. Arrange on a plate.

3. Swirl sugar through yogurt and smatana and serve with fruit.

Hawaiian Crispbreads

Serves 1

2 x 20g (¾oz) rashers lean streaky bacon
2 Ryvita Original crispbreads
½ -1 tsp Marmite
2 small tomatoes, sliced
1 ring pineapple, canned in natural juice, drained, cut into 4
2 sprigs parsley, to garnish

1. Cook the bacon under a preheated grill for 5-6 minutes, until cooked. Discard any excess fat.

2. Meanwhile spread Ryvita Original crispbreads thinly with Marmite and top with tomatoes. Place under the grill for 1-2 minutes to heat tomatoes.

3. Place bacon and pineapple on top of tomatoes and serve garnished with parsley.

Crab Snackers*

Serves 1

50g (2oz) crabmeat
2 tbsp chopped red pepper
4 button mushrooms, chopped
1 tbsp reduced calorie mayonnaise
salt and freshly ground black pepper
2 Ryvita Oat Bran crispbreads
2 stuffed olives, sliced
5 chicory leaves

1. Mix the crabmeat, red pepper, mushrooms and mayonnaise together and season to taste.

2. Divide crab mix between two Ryvita Oat Bran crispbreads and top with sliced stuffed olives.

3. Serve with chicory.

Trout Platter*

Serves 1

75g (3oz) smoked trout
2 tbsp low fat natural yogurt
1 tbsp horseradish sauce
¼ small head curly endive
50g (2oz) mandarin segments, canned in natural juice, drained
10 slices cucumber
50g (2oz) fennel bulb, sliced
1 tbsp fresh chopped dill

1. Break smoked trout into bite size pieces. Mix yogurt and horseradish sauce together and place in a small dish.

2. Arrange curly endive, mandarins, cucumber, fennel and trout on a serving plate and sprinkle with dill.

3. Serve smoked trout platter with horseradish dressing.

Fruity Porridge

Serves 1

15g (2 tbsp) porridge oats
150 ml (¼ pt) skimmed milk
3 no need to soak dried apricots, chopped
2 dried dates, stoned and chopped
1 tbsp strained Greek style yogurt
1 tsp clear honey

1. Place the porridge oats in a small non-stick pan, add the milk and bring to the boil, stirring.

2. Simmer for 3 minutes, remove from heat and stir in the chopped apricots and dates.

3. Transfer to a serving bowl, top with yogurt and honey and serve.

Speedy Starter

Serves 1

1 small banana, sliced
2 tsp wheat germ
2 tbsp low fat natural yogurt
200 ml (7 floz) buttermilk
1 Ryvita Original crispbread
2 tsp low sugar jam

1. Place the banana, wheat germ, yogurt and half the buttermilk in a food processor or blender and purée.

2. Add the remaining buttermilk and process until frothy. Pour into a glass.

3. Serve with a Ryvita Original crispbread, spread with low sugar jam.

200
CALORIES
per serving

Hearty Vegetable Soup*

Serves 1

1 small onion, finely chopped
1 small potato, diced
1 carrot, sliced
1 small leek, sliced
1 tomato, peeled and chopped
300 ml (½ pt) vegetable stock
½ tsp dried mixed herbs
1 tbsp tomato purée
50g (2oz) frozen peas
1 Ryvita Oat Bran crispbread
1 tsp low fat spread with mature Cheddar

1. Place the onion, potato, carrot, leek, tomato, stock, mixed herbs and tomato purée in a saucepan.

2. Bring to the boil, stirring occasionally. Half cover and simmer for 15 minutes, or until vegetables are just tender.

3. Add the peas, re-cover and cook for 5 minutes.

4. Serve soup with a Ryvita Oat Bran crispbread, topped with low fat spread with mature Cheddar.

Piquant Chicken Bites*

Serves 1

50g (2oz) cooked chicken, diced
1 tbsp sweetcorn kernels, defrosted if frozen
2 tsp reduced calorie mayonnaise
salt and freshly ground black pepper
3-4 dashes Tabasco
12 slices cucumber
2 Ryvita Dark Rye crispbreads

1. Mix chicken, sweetcorn and mayonnaise together. Season with salt and pepper and Tabasco.

2. Arrange cucumber slices on top of crispbreads.

3. Top with chicken mix and serve.

Kedgeree

Serves 1

25g (1oz) long grain rice
salt and cayenne pepper
75g (3oz) smoked haddock, skinned
1 hard boiled egg, shelled and chopped
¼ tsp grated nutmeg
1 tbsp lemon juice
1 tbsp fresh chopped parsley
lime wedges, to garnish
2 Ryvita Dark Rye crispbreads

1. Place the rice in a pan of boiling salted water and simmer for 12 minutes or until rice is tender.

2. Meanwhile, place haddock in a pan; barely cover with water and poach for 7-10 minutes or until fish flakes easily.

3. Drain excess water from rice. Drain and flake fish, discarding any bones. Add to rice with egg, salt, cayenne, nutmeg and lemon juice. Heat gently, stirring for 1-2 minutes.

4. Sprinkle with parsley and garnish with lime. Serve with Ryvita Dark Rye crispbreads.

Savoury Breakfast Omelette

Serves 1

2 eggs
salt and freshly ground black pepper
1 tsp vegetable oil
50g (2oz) button mushrooms, sliced
1 small onion, chopped
25g (1oz) lean ham, cut into strips
2 tomatoes, cut into wedges
1 tsp fresh parsley, chopped

1. Beat the eggs together with 15 ml (1 tbsp) cold water and set aside.

2. Brush a non-stick pan with a little oil. Add mushrooms and onion and sauté for 4-5 minutes.

3. Brush a non-stick omelette pan with remaining oil, heat until hot; add eggs and stir gently to draw cooked mixture from sides to centre. Stop stirring when eggs are almost set. Cook for 1 minute to brown.

4. Meanwhile add ham and tomatoes to onions and heat through. Place on omelette, fold over and serve, sprinkled with parsley.

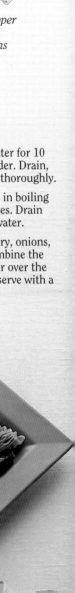

Prawn and Feta Baked Potato

Serves 1

175g (6oz) potato, scrubbed
25g (1oz) peeled prawns
25g (1oz) Feta cheese, crumbled
1 spring onion, chopped
¼ red pepper, diced
1 tbsp strained Greek style yogurt
1 tsp chilli sauce
salad leaves, to garnish

1. Prick the potato and place on a baking sheet. Bake in a preheated oven at 200°C/400°F/Gas 6 for 45-60 minutes, or until tender.

2. Meanwhile mix prawns, cheese, onion, pepper, yogurt and chilli sauce together.

3. Cut horizontal slice from the top of the potato. Fluff up the centre and make a slight well in the middle. Fill with prawn mix and serve, garnished with salad leaves.

Tuna Pasta Salad*

300 CALORIES per serving

Serves 1

25g (1oz) pasta twists
salt and freshly ground black pepper
50g (2oz) broccoli florets
75g (3oz) canned red kidney beans
1 stick celery, sliced
2 spring onions, chopped
50g (2oz) tuna in brine, drained
2 tbsp fresh coriander, chopped
1 clove garlic, crushed
2 tbsp oil free French dressing
1 Ryvita Sesame crispbread

1. Cook pasta in boiling salted water for 10 minutes or until pasta is just tender. Drain, rinse under cold water and drain thoroughly.

2. Meanwhile blanch the broccoli in boiling lightly salted water for 3-4 minutes. Drain and refresh under cold running water.

3. Mix pasta, broccoli, beans, celery, onions, tuna and coriander together. Combine the garlic and salad dressing and pour over the salad. Toss together, season and serve with a Ryvita Sesame crispbread.

Breakfast Mushrooms

Serves 1

100g (4oz) open cap mushrooms
1 tsp vegetable oil
1 rasher bacon, chopped
1 egg, lightly beaten
1 tbsp skimmed milk
salt and freshly ground black pepper
parsley, to garnish
2 Ryvita Sesame crispbreads
1 tsp very low fat spread

1. Remove stalks from mushrooms and chop. Heat oil in a non-stick frying pan and add mushroom caps and bacon. Cook 2-3 minutes. Add chopped mushrooms and cook for a further 2-3 minutes.

2. Mix egg, milk and seasoning together. Remove mushroom caps from pan. Add egg to pan and cook for 2-3 minutes until egg has set.

3. Spoon egg and bacon mix into mushroom caps and garnish with parsley. Serve with Ryvita Sesame crispbreads topped with very low fat spread.

Demon Kidneys

Serves 1

2 lambs' kidneys
2 tsp Worcestershire sauce
1 tsp French mustard
1 tbsp lemon juice
1 tbsp tomato purée
dash of Tabasco
salt and freshly ground black pepper
2 tsp sunflower oil
2 tomatoes, quartered
fresh chopped parsley, to garnish
2 Ryvita Sesame crispbreads

1. Remove the skin from the kidneys and cut in half. Cut away the core.

2. Mix together the Worcestershire sauce, mustard, lemon juice, tomato purée, Tabasco and seasoning.

3. Heat the oil in a small non-stick frying pan over a medium heat. Add kidneys and fry for about 3 minutes per side.

4. Pour over the Worcestershire sauce mix and cook for 1 minute, stirring to coat kidneys. Serve with tomatoes, parsley and Ryvita Sesame crispbreads.

Baked Cheese Specials

Serves 1

1 tsp vegetable oil
1 onion, finely chopped
½ red pepper, chopped
100g (4oz) cottage cheese with chives
25g (1oz) peeled prawns or tuna in brine, drained
1 egg, beaten
salt
½ tsp paprika
2 Ryvita Original or Dark Rye crispbreads

1. Heat the oil in a small pan, add the onion and pepper and fry gently for 4-5 minutes until softened.

2. Remove from heat and stir in cheese, prawns or tuna, egg, salt and paprika.

3. Place in a shallow oven-proof dish and bake in a preheated oven at 200°C/400°F/Gas 6 for 30 minutes until golden.

4. Serve with 2 Ryvita crispbreads.

Tabbouleh*

Serves 1

40g (1½ oz) cracked bulghur wheat
2 spring onions, chopped
2 tomatoes, chopped
2 tbsp chopped fresh parsley
1 tbsp chopped fresh mint
1 small clove garlic, crushed
1 tbsp lemon juice
1 tbsp olive oil
5 cm (2 in) piece cucumber, diced
salt and freshly ground black pepper
15g (½ oz) roquefort cheese, crumbled
1 Ryvita Dark Rye crispbread

1. Place bulghur wheat in a bowl. Cover with boiling water and leave to soak for 20 minutes. Drain if necessary.

2. Mix onions, tomatoes, parsley, mint, garlic, lemon juice, olive oil and cucumber together.

3. Stir in bulghur wheat and season to taste. Chill.

4. Serve topped with roquefort cheese with Ryvita Dark Rye crispbread.

Tomato and Onion Salad*

Serves 1

2 tomatoes, sliced
½ onion, sliced and separated into rings
3 black olives
2 tbsp oil free French dressing
salt and freshly ground black pepper
1 tsp chopped fresh parsley
1 Ryvita Sesame crispbread
1 tbsp cottage cheese

1. Arrange tomatoes, onion and olives on a plate.

2. Sprinkle with French dressing and seasoning and sprinkle with parsley.

3. Top Ryvita Sesame crispbread with cheese and serve with tomato and onion salad.

Stuffed Pears*

Serves 1

1 ripe dessert pear
1 tbsp lemon juice
50g (2oz) cottage cheese with pineapple
1 walnut half, chopped
radicchio leaves, to serve

1. Wash and halve the pear. Scoop out and discard the seeds and scoop out flesh to leave a 2·5 cm (1 in) shell.

2. Brush shell with lemon juice. Chop remaining pear and toss with remaining lemon juice. Mix with cottage cheese and pile into pear shells.

3. Sprinkle chopped walnuts over the top and serve on a bed of radicchio leaves.

100
CALORIES
per serving

Mixed Fruit Terrine

Serves 4

75g (3oz) grapes, halved
150g (5oz) small strawberries, halved
1 small mango, peeled, stoned and chopped
3 tsp powdered gelatine
350 ml (12 floz) fresh orange juice
225g (8oz) frozen raspberries, defrosted
1 tbsp icing sugar

1. Mix fruit together and place in a 450g (1lb) non stick loaf tin.

2. Sprinkle gelatine over 3 tbsp orange juice and leave to stand for 5 minutes. Heat gently to dissolve and stir in remaining orange juice.

3. Pour over fruit and chill until set. Meanwhile purée raspberries and icing sugar in a food processor. Sieve to remove seeds.

4. Dip tin into hot water and invert on to a plate to unmould. Serve whole or sliced with raspberry sauce.

Rhubarb Flummery

Serves 4

450g (1lb) rhubarb, cut into 2·5 cm
(1 in) lengths
¼ tsp ground ginger
40g (1½oz) caster sugar
juice and grated rind 1 orange
1 sachet powdered gelatine
2 pieces stem ginger, finely chopped
2 egg whites
2 tbsp soured cream and lemon geranium leaves, optional, to decorate

1. Place the rhubarb, ground ginger, sugar, orange juice and rind in a saucepan and simmer gently for about 10 minutes until fruit is tender.

2. Sprinkle gelatine over 2 tbsp water and leave to swell for 5 minutes. Stir into the hot rhubarb. Beat until smooth and cool.

3. Chill until starting to set, then fold in the stem ginger. Whisk the egg whites until stiff and lightly fold into rhubarb mix.

4. Divide between four glasses and chill until set. Serve topped with soured cream and lemon geranium leaves, if wished.

Easy Carrot Soup*

Serves 1

100g (4oz) carrots, diced
1 small onion, chopped
1 stick celery, chopped
300 ml (½ pt) vegetable stock
salt and freshly ground black pepper
1 tsp ground cumin
grated rind and juice ½ orange
chopped fresh parsley or coriander, to garnish
2 Ryvita Dark Rye crispbreads

1. Place carrot, onion, celery and stock in a saucepan. Stir in seasoning and cumin and bring to the boil.

2. Cover and simmer for 20 minutes or until carrots are tender. Cool slightly and purée until smooth.

3. Return to pan, add rind and orange juice and reheat. Garnish with coriander and serve with Ryvita Dark Rye crispbreads.

Devilled Mushrooms

Serves 1

100g (4oz) button mushrooms, halved
2 tbsp tomato purée
dash Tabasco or ½ tsp chilli powder
salt and freshly ground black pepper
2 Ryvita Sesame crispbreads

1. Place the mushrooms in a small saucepan with tomato purée, 1 tbsp water, Tabasco or chilli powder and seasoning.

2. Cook for 4-5 minutes or until mushrooms are cooked, and sauce is thick.

3. Serve mushrooms on Ryvita Sesame crispbreads.

Apple and Kiwi Sorbet

Serves 4

4 kiwi fruit
300 ml (½ pt) fresh apple juice
2 tbsp clear honey
1 egg white
mint leaves, to decorate

1. Peel 2 kiwi and mash to a purée with a fork. Mix with apple juice and honey. Chill for 30 minutes.

2. Stir and pour into a shallow freezer-proof container. Freeze for 1 to 2 hours until slushy.

3. Whisk egg white until fairly stiff. Transfer kiwi mix to a bowl, and beat to break up ice crystals. Fold in egg white. Return to freezer and freeze for about 2 hours until firm.

4. To serve, transfer to refrigerator for 10-15 minutes to soften. Slice remaining kiwis. Serve scoops of sorbet with sliced kiwis.

Summer Compote

100 CALORIES per serving

Serves 4

100g (4oz) blackcurrants
40g (1½oz) caster sugar
125 ml (4 floz) fresh orange juice
1 tsp arrowroot
100g (4oz) raspberries
225g (8oz) strawberries
3 tbsp strained Greek style yogurt

1. Place blackcurrants in a pan with the sugar and orange juice. Bring to the boil, then cover and simmer gently for 5-6 minutes, until softened. Remove from heat.

2. Mix the arrowroot with 2 tbsp water and add to the pan. Stir well and return to heat. Bring to the boil stirring until sauce has thickened.

3. Add raspberries and strawberries and leave to cool.

4. Serve chilled in individual glasses, each topped with 2 tsp Greek yogurt.

Prawn and Cucumber Dip*

Serves 1

3 tbsp low fat natural yogurt
1 tbsp fresh mint, chopped
1 tsp lemon juice
5 cm (2 in) piece cucumber
1 carrot, peeled
1 stick celery
50g (2oz) peeled prawns
1 Ryvita Dark Rye crispbread

1. Mix the yogurt, mint and lemon juice together.

2. Cut cucumber, carrot and celery into sticks.

3. Arrange mint and yogurt dip on a plate with prawns, vegetables and Ryvita Dark Rye crispbread.

Chocolate and Strawberry Crispbread*

Serves 1

1 Ryvita Original crispbread
2 tsp hazelnut chocolate spread
50g (2oz) strawberries

1. Spread crispbread with hazelnut chocolate spread.

2. Cut strawberries into slices and arrange on top of crispbread.

Mini Meringue Nests

Serves 4

1 small eating apple
1 tbsp clear honey
100g (4oz) blackberries
2 tsp arrowroot
50g (2oz) raspberries
4 meringue nests
redcurrants, to decorate, optional

1. Core and slice the apple. Place the honey in a small pan with 90 ml (3 floz) water and bring to the boil.

2. Add the apple and blackberries and simmer for 3-5 minutes until just softened. Mix the arrowroot with 1 tbsp water and stir into the pan to thicken juices.

3. Remove from the heat, stir in the raspberries and leave to cool. Chill.

4. To serve, spoon the fruit into the meringue nests and serve immediately, decorated with redcurrants.

Vanilla Cloud

Serves 4

250 ml (8 floz) skimmed milk
2 eggs, separated
4 tsp caster sugar
½ tsp vanilla essence
2 tsp powdered gelatine
75g (3oz) raspberries
1 kiwi, sliced
75g (3oz) strawberries, sliced

1. Place milk in a saucepan and bring to the boil. Meanwhile mix egg yolks, sugar and vanilla together.

2. Pour milk on to egg yolk mix and stir well. Return to pan and heat gently until mixture coats back of spoon. Do not boil. Remove from heat and leave to cool.

3. Sprinkle gelatine over 2 tbsp water in a small bowl. Leave for 5 minutes, then place the bowl in a pan of boiling water and stir to dissolve.

4. Stir gelatine into custard and chill until it begins to thicken. Whisk egg whites until stiff, then fold into custard.

5. Reserve 4 raspberries. Mix remaining fruit together and place in 4 glasses, top with vanilla custard and chill for 1 hour. Serve decorated with reserved raspberries.

100 CALORIES per serving

Gazpacho*

Serves 1

150 ml (¼ pt) tomato juice
1 tomato, chopped
1 small clove garlic, crushed
½ small onion, chopped
2·5 cm (1 in) cucumber, chopped
½ green pepper
2 tsp white wine vinegar
salt and freshly ground black pepper
1 spring onion, chopped
2 Ryvita Dark Rye crispbreads

1. Place the tomato juice, tomato, garlic, onion, cucumber and pepper in a food processor or blender and process until puréed.

2. Whisk in the vinegar and seasoning. Pour into a bowl and top with spring onion.

3. Serve chilled with Ryvita Dark Rye crispbreads.

Fruit and Nut Crunch*

Serves 1

1 Ryvita Oat Bran crispbread
1 tsp clear honey
½ apple
2 tsp sultanas or raisins
1 tsp chopped hazelnuts

1. Spread the Ryvita Oat Bran crispbread with honey.

2. Slice the apple and arrange on top of the crispbread.

3. Mix the sultanas or raisins with the hazelnuts and sprinkle over the apples.

Orange Granita

Serves 4

1 x 200g (7oz) carton frozen orange juice concentrate
4 tsp low calorie concentrated blackcurrant juice drink

1. Defrost concentrated fruit juice until just melted. Mix with 350 ml (12 floz) water. Pour into a shallow freezer tray and freeze for 1-1½ hours until almost hard.

2. Using a metal fork break up into crystals. Either spoon the crystals into a freezer bag, seal and return to the freezer, or re-freeze for 10-15 minutes before serving.

3. To serve, chill 4 glasses, spoon crystals into each glass and top each with a teaspoon of blackcurrant juice drink.

Fresh Fruit Dip

Serves 4

3 x 110g (4oz) pots virtually fat free peach, melon or black cherry yogurt
110g (4oz) low fat skimmed milk soft cheese (quark)
1 tbsp kirsch
450g (1lb) mixed fresh fruit e.g. melon, oranges, grapes, strawberries, cherries or pineapple.

1. Mix the yogurt, cheese and kirsch together and place in a serving bowl. Chill.

2. Cube melon, segment oranges, wash grapes, strawberries and cherries, and slice pineapple, depending on choice of fruits.

3. Arrange fruits on a large serving plate with dip in the centre. Serve.

Cheese Toppers*

Serves 1

25g (1oz) low fat Edam cheese, cubed
25g (1oz) low fat cottage cheese with
pineapple
1 stick celery, chopped
2·5 cm (1 in) piece cucumber, chopped
1 small red apple
1 tsp lemon juice
2 Ryvita Oat Bran crispbreads

1. Mix the cheeses, celery and cucumber together.

2. Cut the apple in half, dice half and toss in lemon juice. Add to cheese mixture. Slice remaining apple.

3. Top Ryvita Oat Bran crispbreads with cheese mix and serve with apple slices.

Cheese and Tomato Toasties

Serves 1

2 tomatoes, sliced
2 Ryvita Original crispbreads
25g (1oz) Cheddar cheese, grated
1 tsp skimmed milk
½ tsp French mustard
½ tsp paprika
salad leaves, to garnish

1. Arrange tomato slices on top of crispbreads.

2. Mix cheese, milk, mustard and paprika together. Spread over tomatoes.

3. Place under a preheated grill and cook until cheese melts.

4. Serve immediately garnished with salad leaves.

Banana Special

Serves 4

25g (1oz) unsalted butter
juice and grated rind 1 orange
1 tsp ground cinnamon
4 firm bananas, peeled and quartered
50g (2oz) light muscovado sugar
4 tbsp rum
1 tbsp flaked hazelnuts

1. Melt the butter in a frying pan, add the orange juice, cinnamon and bananas and cook for 3-4 minutes until just softened.

2. Add the sugar and stir until dissolved. Add the rum, carefully set alight. Stir gently to mix.

3. Decorate bananas with grated orange rind and hazelnuts and serve immediately.

Cappucino Custards

Serves 4

575 ml (1 pt) semi-skimmed milk
4 eggs
25g (1oz) demerara sugar
4 tsp instant coffee
1 egg white
1 tbsp caster sugar
1 tsp cocoa powder

1. Heat the milk until hot. Meanwhile whisk the eggs and demerara sugar together. Add the milk and coffee and whisk thoroughly.

2. Preheat oven to 180°C/350°F/Gas 4. Pour into four oven-proof dishes. Stand the dishes in a small roasting tin filled with sufficient water to come halfway up the sides of the dishes.

3. Bake for 15-20 minutes or until set. Whisk the egg white and caster sugar together until stiff. Spoon or pipe on to custards. Sprinkle with cocoa powder.

4. Return to the oven for 5-10 minutes to set the meringue. Serve.

Italian Melts

Serves 1

2 Ryvita Dark Rye crispbreads
2 tsp pesto sauce
40g (1½ oz) chèvre cheese, sliced into two
1 small tomato, sliced
basil leaves, to garnish

1. Spread crispbreads with pesto sauce. Cut cheese in half and place on top of crispbreads.

2. Place under a preheated grill and cook until cheese melts and browns slightly.

3. Top with tomato and basil and serve.

Tuna Pâté Salad*

Serves 1

75g (3oz) tuna in brine
2 tbsp strained Greek style yogurt
juice and grated rind ½ lemon
2 tsp snipped chives
salt and freshly ground black pepper
salad leaves
2 Ryvita Original crispbreads

1. Place tuna and yogurt in a blender and blend until smooth. Alternatively flake tuna and blend with yogurt for a coarser textured pâté.

2. Add lemon juice and rind, chives and seasoning and chill for 15 minutes.

3. Arrange salad leaves on a plate and top with pâté. Serve with crispbreads.

Cheesy Fruit Cups

Serves 4

1 banana
100g (4oz) whole seedless grapes, halved
1 orange, peeled and segmented
1 mango, peeled, stoned and diced
100g (4oz) curd cheese
150g (5·3oz) carton low fat natural yogurt
1 tbsp caster sugar
2 tbsp flaked almonds, toasted

1. Slice banana, add grapes, orange and mango and toss together.

2. Mix curd cheese, yogurt and sugar together. Add fruit and mix together.

3. Spoon into individual dishes, top with almonds and serve.

Apricot Rice Pots

Serves 4

50g (2oz) pudding rice
500 ml (17 floz) semi-skimmed milk
2 tbsp sugar
40g (1½oz) sultanas
1 tsp grated nutmeg
4 apricots, sliced to decorate

1. Place the rice, milk and sugar in a heavy based saucepan and bring to the boil. Simmer gently for 20 minutes until it begins to thicken, stirring occasionally.

2. Preheat oven to 200°C/400°F/Gas 6. Lightly grease 4 small oven-proof dishes. Mix sultanas into rice and divide rice mixture between dishes.

3. Bake for 20 minutes until lightly golden. Sprinkle with nutmeg and serve warm, decorated with apricot slices.

Beef and Vegetable Pie

Serves 4

675g (1½lb) potatoes, peeled
salt and freshly ground black pepper
3 tbsp skimmed milk
450g (1lb) lean minced beef
2 onions, chopped
2 carrots, diced
4 heaped tsp gravy granules
225g (8oz) broccoli florets, cooked and
225g (8oz) leeks, sliced and cooked, to serve

1. Cook the potatoes in boiling salted water for 15-20 minutes, then drain and mash with milk and seasoning.

2. Meanwhile, dry fry the beef, then add the onions, carrots, gravy granules and 300 ml (½ pt) water.

3. Bring to the boil, stirring, then cover and simmer for 30 minutes. Season to taste. Transfer to an oven-proof dish and top with potato.

4. Bake in a preheated oven at 190°C/375°F/Gas 5 for 30 minutes, until potato has browned. Serve with broccoli and leeks.

Seafood Pasta

Serves 4

2 tsp olive oil
1 onion, sliced
1 clove garlic, crushed
400g (14oz) can chopped tomatoes
1 tbsp tomato purée
100g (4oz) button mushrooms
2 sticks celery, sliced
100g (4oz) broccoli florets
225g (8oz) green and white tagliatelle
198g (7½oz) can tuna in brine, drained
100g (4oz) peeled prawns
100g (4oz) shelled cooked mussels
salt and freshly ground black pepper
chopped fresh herbs, to garnish

1. Heat the oil in a non-stick pan, add the onion and garlic and cook for 4-5 minutes until softened.

2. Add the tomatoes, tomato purée, mushrooms, celery and broccoli and bring to the boil. Cover and simmer for 10 minutes.

3. Meanwhile cook tagliatelle in boiling salted water for 8-10 minutes, or until just tender.

4. Add tuna, prawns and mussels to sauce and heat through. Season to taste.

5. Drain tagliatelle and serve, topped with seafood sauce. Garnish with herbs.

Gammon and Pineapple Pizza

Serves 4

6 Ryvita Dark Rye crispbreads, crushed
110g (4oz) strong plain flour
½ sachet easy blend dried yeast
2 tbsp olive oil
225g (8oz) can chopped tomatoes
2 tsp dried oregano
salt and freshly ground black pepper
175g (6oz) lean gammon steak, diced
225g (8oz) pineapple pieces in fruit juice, drained
1 green pepper, seeded and sliced
100g (4oz) mozzarella cheese, grated
mixed salad leaves with oil free dressing, to serve

1. Mix the Ryvita, flour and yeast together in a food processor. Add the olive oil and 75-100 ml (3-4 floz) lukewarm water and mix to a smooth dough. Knead on a floured board until smooth and elastic.

2. Roll out dough into a 23 cm (9 in) round and place on a baking tray. Spread tomatoes over base and sprinkle with oregano and seasoning.

3. Top with gammon, pineapple, pepper and cheese. Bake in a preheated oven at 220°C/425°F/Gas 7 for 20-25 minutes. Serve with mixed salad leaves.

Warm Chinese Salad

Serves 4

4 x 140g (5oz) skinless chicken breast fillets
5 tsp clear honey
2 tbsp dry sherry
3 tbsp soy sauce
2 tbsp sesame oil
1 tbsp orange juice
225g (8oz) bean-sprouts
½ red pepper, seeded, cut into thin strips
½ green pepper, seeded, cut into thin strips
2 sticks celery, sliced
¼ head Chinese leaves, shredded
325g (12oz) baby new potatoes, boiled, to serve

1. Cut each chicken breast into three. Mix 3 tsp honey, 1 tbsp sherry, 2 tbsp soy sauce, 1 tbsp sesame oil and orange juice together. Pour over chicken and leave to marinade for 30 minutes. Leave longer if time allows.

2. Place chicken on a roasting rack and cook in a preheated oven at 200°C/400°F/Gas 6 for 15-20 minutes, until juices run clear.

3. Meanwhile mix bean sprouts, peppers, celery and Chinese leaves together. Combine remaining honey, sherry, soy sauce and sesame oil together in a small pan and heat gently until hot.

4. Pour dressing over vegetables and serve with chicken.

Italian Fish Casserole

Serves 4

2 onions, sliced
1 clove garlic, crushed
1 tbsp olive oil
2 tbsp plain flour
2 tsp paprika
300 ml (½ pt) dry white wine
400g (14oz) can chopped tomatoes
salt and freshly ground black pepper
1 tsp mixed herbs
225g (8oz) courgettes, sliced
550g (1¼lb) firm white fish e.g. haddock,
cod, monkfish
100g (4oz) shelled, cooked mussels
185g (6½oz) can pimientos, drained and
sliced
4 x 175g (6oz) baked potatoes and
450g (1lb) green beans, boiled, to serve

1. Sauté the onions and garlic in the oil until
soft and transparent. Stir in the flour and
paprika.

2. Stir in the wine, chopped tomatoes,
seasoning and herbs and bring to the boil,
stirring. Simmer for 5 minutes.

3. Add the courgettes and fish. Cover and
simmer for 15 minutes. Stir in mussels and
pimientos and cook for a further 5 minutes.
Serve with baked potatoes and green beans.

Chicken Korma

Serves 4

150g (5oz) natural low fat yogurt
1 tsp turmeric
1 tsp ground coriander
2·5 cm (1 in) piece fresh root ginger, finely
chopped
450g (1lb) chicken breast fillets, cut into
large pieces
1 onion, chopped
40g (1½oz) flaked almonds
1 tsp chilli powder
1 tbsp olive oil
salt and freshly ground black pepper
175g (6oz) basmati rice, cooked and mixed
with chopped fresh coriander, to serve

1. Mix yogurt, turmeric, coriander and
ginger together. Add chicken, coat and leave
to stand for 30 minutes, or longer if time
allows.

2. Mix onion, almonds, chilli and 150 ml
(¼ pt) water together in a blender until
almost smooth. Lift chicken from marinade
and fry in the oil until browned.

3. Gradually stir in marinade and then stir in
nut mixture. Bring to the boil, season and
simmer for 20-30 minutes. Serve with rice.

Beef Stir Fry

Serves 4

450g (1lb) lean rump or minute steak, cut into strips
4 tbsp soy sauce
4 tbsp dry sherry
2 cloves garlic, crushed
2·5 cm (1 in) piece fresh root ginger, grated
2 tbsp sunflower oil
4 sticks celery, sliced
100g (4oz) French beans, cut into 2·5 cm (1 in) lengths
150g (5oz) oyster or chestnut mushrooms, halved
1 tsp cornflour
Chinese egg noodles, cooked, to serve

1. Place the beef in a shallow dish. Mix the soy sauce, sherry, garlic and ginger together. Add to the beef, toss to coat, cover and leave for 30 minutes.

2. Heat the oil in a wok or heavy based frying pan. Drain the meat, reserving marinade and stir fry beef for 3 minutes. Add the celery, French beans and stir fry for 2 minutes.

3. Add the mushrooms and stir fry for 2-3 minutes. Blend cornflour with reserved marinade, pour into the wok and stir well. Serve with Chinese egg noodles.

Lamb Medley

Serves 4

1 tbsp olive oil
450g (1lb) lean lamb fillet or boneless loin, cut into large chunks
100g (4oz) mangetout
100g (4oz) baby sweetcorn
2 tsp cornflour
200 ml (7 floz) vegetable stock
1 tbsp concentrated mint sauce
2 tbsp redcurrant jelly
salt and freshly ground black pepper
450g (1lb) mashed potato, to serve

1. Heat the oil in a non stick pan, add the lamb and cook for 4-5 minutes, to brown.

2. Add the mangetout and sweetcorn and stir fry for 2-3 minutes. Mix the cornflour with a little vegetable stock, then mix in the remainder. Add to the pan with mint sauce and redcurrant jelly.

3. Bring to the boil, stirring until thickened. Simmer for 2-3 minutes, until vegetables are tender crisp, season and serve with mashed potato.

Pork Fillet with Oranges

Serves 4

450g (1lb) lean pork fillet
1 tbsp Dijon mustard
2 tbsp fresh breadcrumbs
2 tbsp fresh chopped tarragon
1 tbsp fresh chopped parsley
salt and freshly ground black pepper
2 tsp cornflour
150 ml (5 floz) fresh orange juice
150 ml (5 floz) dry white wine or vegetable stock
1 tsp ground coriander
2 oranges, peeled and segmented
4 x 140g (5oz) baked potatoes topped with 4 tbsp smetana and 450g (1lb) Brussels sprouts or broccoli, boiled, to serve

1. Place pork in a roasting dish. Spread with mustard. Mix breadcrumbs, herbs and seasoning together and coat the pork.

2. Cook in a preheated oven at 200°C/400°F/Gas 6 for 40-45 minutes, or until juices run clear. Meanwhile blend cornflour with a little orange juice. Add remaining juice, wine and coriander.

3. Bring sauce to the boil, stirring until thickened. Stir in the orange segments and season. Serve pork with sauce, and vegetables.

Turkey and Cider Hot Pot

Serves 4

2 leeks, sliced
225g (8oz) button mushrooms, sliced
2 tbsp sunflower oil
25g (1oz) seasoned flour
300 ml (½ pt) chicken stock
150 ml (¼ pt) dry cider
450g (1lb) turkey breast fillets, cut into chunks
1 tsp fresh sage, chopped
1 eating apple, cored and sliced
550g (1¼lb) potatoes, sliced
450g (1lb) mixed courgettes and carrots, boiled, to serve

1. Fry the leeks and mushrooms in 1 tbsp oil, for 4-5 minutes. Stir in the flour, then add the stock and cider. Bring to the boil, stirring until thickened.

2. Add the turkey and cook for 4-5 minutes. Stir in the sage and apple and transfer to a casserole dish. Cook potatoes in boiling salted water for 5 minutes. Drain, cool slightly and arrange over the top of the casserole.

3. Brush with remaining oil and bake in a preheated oven at 190°C/375°F/Gas 5 for 45-55 minutes until golden and tender. Serve with courgettes and carrots.

Filo Fish Pie

Serves 4

50g (2oz) butter
1 onion, chopped
100g (4oz) button mushrooms, sliced
25g (1oz) plain flour
350 ml (12 floz) vegetable stock
450g (1lb) haddock fillet, skinned and cut into chunks
2 tsp chopped fresh sage
salt and freshly ground black pepper
200g (7oz) can whole artichokes, drained and quartered
100g (4oz) peeled prawns
125g (4½oz) filo pastry
4 Ryvita Dark Rye crispbreads
2 tbsp grated Parmesan cheese

1. Melt 15g (½oz) butter, add onions and mushrooms and sauté for 3-4 minutes. Stir in the flour, then gradually add the stock. Bring to the boil, stirring until thickened.

2. Add fish, sage, seasoning and cook for 4-5 minutes. Add artichokes and prawns. Transfer to a shallow pie dish. Leave to cool.

3. Melt remaining butter, brush over pastry and arrange on pie filling. Bake in a preheated oven at 200°C/400°F/Gas 6 for 20-25 minutes, until crisp and golden.

4. Sprinkle Ryvita with cheese and toast until golden. Serve with fish pie.

Spicy Chicken Kebabs

Serves 4

450g (1lb) chicken breast fillets
1 tbsp satay marinade mix
2 tbsp soy sauce
2 tbsp olive oil
1 red pepper, seeded
1 green pepper, seeded
200g (7oz) long grain white rice
salt
½ tsp turmeric
mixed salad, to serve

1. Cut chicken into 2·5 cm (1 in) cubes. Combine satay mix with soy sauce and 1 tbsp olive oil. Add meat and toss to coat. Leave to stand for 30 minutes.

2. Cut peppers into 2·5 cm (1 in) cubes. Thread meat onto skewers alternating with peppers. Cook under a preheated grill for 10-15 minutes. Turn and brush with remaining oil, as required.

3. Meanwhile cook the rice in a pan of boiling salted water with turmeric for 12 minutes, until tender. Drain. Serve kebabs with rice and mixed salad.

Tuna Macaroni Bake

Serves 4

175g (6oz) short cut macaroni
25g (1oz) margarine
1 tbsp sunflower oil
40g (1½oz) plain flour
700 ml (1¼ pt) skimmed milk
2 leeks, chopped
185g (6½oz) can tuna chunks in spring
water, drained and flaked
75g (3oz) low calorie Cheddar style cheese,
grated
salt and freshly ground black pepper
25g (1oz) mature Cheddar cheese, grated
4 Ryvita Sesame crispbreads
fennel, tomato and black olive salad, to serve

1. Cook macaroni in a large pan of boiling water for 10 minutes until just tender. Meanwhile heat the margarine and oil together, stir in the flour, then gradually stir in the milk.

2. Bring to the boil, stirring continuously, until thickened. Add the leeks and cook for 4-5 minutes. Stir in the tuna, Cheddar style cheese and season.

3. Drain macaroni and stir in. Transfer to a heatproof dish, sprinkle with Cheddar cheese and grill lightly until cheese melts. Serve with Ryvita Sesame crispbreads and salad.

Chicken and Vegetable Risotto

Serves 4

1 aubergine, diced
salt and freshly ground black pepper
2 tbsp olive oil
1 onion, chopped
225g (8oz) chicken livers, chopped
225g (8oz) chicken breast fillets, diced
2 rashers lean back bacon, cut into strips
225g (8oz) long grain rice
½ yellow and ½ green pepper, seeded and
chopped
225g (8oz) tomatoes, skinned and chopped
750 ml (1¼ pt) vegetable stock
50g (2oz) cashew nuts
1 tbsp fresh chopped parsley, to garnish

1. Sprinkle aubergine with salt and leave to drain. Heat oil in a large frying pan. Add onion, livers, chicken and bacon and fry for 2-3 minutes.

2. Stir in rice, peppers, tomatoes, stock and cashew nuts. Rinse aubergine and add.

3. Cover and simmer for 20-25 minutes, until rice is tender. Season and serve, garnished with parsley.

Broccoli Cheese Flan

Serves 4

6 Slices Ryvita Sesame crispbreads, crushed
110g (4oz) plain flour
50g (2oz) margarine
2 eggs, lightly beaten
175g (6oz) low fat fromage frais
salt and freshly ground black pepper
50g (2oz) roquefort, crumbled
100g (4oz) small broccoli florets
50g (2oz) button mushrooms, sliced
3 spring onions, chopped
½ red pepper, diced
325g (12oz) new potatoes, boiled and
tomato and onion salad, to serve

1. Mix Ryvita Sesame crispbreads and flour together in a food processor until smooth. Add margarine, mix to form fine breadcrumbs, add 1-2 tbsp cold water and mix to a dough.

2. Roll out pastry and use to line a 20 cm (8 in) flan ring. Bake blind at 190°C/375°F/ Gas 5 for 20 minutes. Remove baking beans.

3. Mix eggs, fromage frais, seasoning, roquefort, broccoli, mushrooms, onions and pepper together. Place in flan case and bake for 30-35 minutes until set and golden.

4. Serve with potatoes and tomato and onion salad.

Chilli Con Carne

Serves 4

450g (1lb) lean minced beef
2 onions, chopped
3 tbsp tomato purée
2 x 400g (14oz) can chopped tomatoes with
garlic and herbs
1-2 tsp chilli powder
440g (16oz) can red kidney beans, drained
salt and freshly ground black pepper
200g (7oz) long grain rice, cooked, to serve
parsley or chilli, to garnish

1. Dry fry the minced beef until cooked. Add the onions, tomato purée, chopped tomatoes and chilli and mix together thoroughly.

2. Bring to the boil, cover and simmer gently for 45 minutes. Stir occasionally.

3. Add the red kidney beans, stir well, adjust seasoning and simmer for 10 minutes.

4. Serve chilli on a bed of boiled rice.

Diet for Life

Once you have reached your target weight
Ryvita doesn't leave you high and dry. In the
next 20 pages of this book are a selection of
recipes to ensure all your good work
won't go to waste.

Once you have completed your slimming
diet, it is important not to slip back into your
old eating habits which encouraged
weight gain.

These recipes have been selected to
complement a healthier lifestyle. They follow
recommended guidelines for a lower fat and
sugar diet and a higher fibre intake. Ryvita
are included in a number of these recipes for
they are a food which follows these
guidelines.

Use these recipes as a basis for your diet from
now on. Include lots of fresh fruits and
vegetables as well.

Combine this diet with taking more exercise
and the new sleeker, fitter you will remain.

Diet for Life Index

Spicy Lentil Soup

Serves 4

110g (4oz) red lentils, washed
1 onion, chopped
1 clove garlic, chopped
225g (8oz) can chopped tomatoes
1 carrot, chopped
1 tsp ground coriander
1 tsp ground cumin
salt and pepper
900 ml (1½pt) vegetable stock
4 Ryvita Sesame crispbreads
50g (2oz) Mozzarella cheese, grated
2 tbsp soured cream

1. Place the lentils, onion, garlic, tomatoes, carrot, coriander, cumin, seasoning and stock in a saucepan and bring to the boil. Cover and simmer for 40-50 minutes until lentils are tender.

2. Cool slightly and lightly purée in a food processor. Sprinkle Ryvita Sesame crispbreads with cheese and place under a preheated grill to melt. Reheat soup and top with soured cream. Serve with crispbreads.

Per serving: Fat: 8g Fibre: 5·5g Calories: 200

Ham and Prawn Rolls

Serves 4

4 large slices or 8 small slices ham
225g (8oz) cottage cheese with chives
50g (2oz) peeled prawns
100g (4oz) pineapple slices in natural juice,
drained and chopped
salt and freshly ground black pepper
4 tsp anchovy fish paste
4 Ryvita Dark Rye crispbreads
cress, to garnish

1. Cut ham slices in half if large. Mix cottage cheese, prawns and pineapple together. Season. Divide between ham and roll up.

2. Spread fish paste on Ryvita Dark Rye crispbreads and top each one with two ham rolls. Garnish with cress and serve.

Per serving: Fat: 11g Fibre: 2g Calories: 165

Tasty Rice Salad

Serves 4

225g (8oz) brown long grain rice
salt
½ tsp ground turmeric
4 rashers lean back bacon
1 tsp garam masala
4 tbsp oil free French dressing
1 red pepper, diced
25g (1oz) sunflower seeds
100g (4oz) sweetcorn kernels
¼ cucumber, diced

1. Cook the rice in a large pan of boiling salted water with turmeric for 25-30 minutes, until tender. Drain, rinse and drain again. Meanwhile, grill bacon until crisp and golden.

2. Add garam masala and French dressing to rice. Toss together and leave to cool. Stir in the pepper, sunflower seeds, sweetcorn and cucumber. Chop bacon and sprinkle over salad.

Per serving: Fat: 2·5g Fibre: 4·5g Calories: 360

Fruity Edam Salad

Serves 4

1 red apple, cored and chopped
75g (3oz) seedless red grapes
1 kiwi, sliced
100g (4oz) Edam cheese, cubed
25g (1oz) pecan nuts
25g (1oz) hazelnuts
3 sticks celery, sliced
50g (2oz) fennel, sliced thinly
2 tbsp strained Greek style yogurt
2 tbsp soured cream
2 tbsp lemon juice
½ head curly endive, torn into pieces

1. Mix apple, grapes, kiwi, cheese, nuts, celery and fennel together.

2. Mix yogurt, soured cream and lemon juice together. Pour over salad and gently toss together. Serve on a bed of curly endive.

Per serving: Fat: 13g Fibre: 4·5g Calories: 240

Stuffed Peppers

Serves 4

4 peppers, cut in half lengthways and seeded
1 tsp sunflower oil
1 onion, finely chopped
100g (4oz) long grain brown rice, cooked
50g (2oz) walnuts, chopped
75g (3oz) no need to soak apricots
75g (3oz) lean ham, diced
1 tbsp chopped fresh coriander
1 tsp ground cumin
salt and freshly ground black pepper
4 Ryvita Dark Rye crispbreads
4 tsp low fat spread

1. Place the peppers in a pan of boiling water and cook for 3 minutes. Drain, and place in a shallow oven-proof dish with a little water.

2. Heat the oil, add the onion and fry for 3-4 minutes to soften. Add the rice, walnuts, apricots, ham, coriander, cumin and season to taste. Use to stuff peppers.

3. Cover tightly with aluminium foil and bake in a preheated oven at 190°C/375°F/Gas 5 for 30 minutes. Serve with Ryvita Dark Rye crispbreads topped with low fat spread.

Per serving: Fat: 13g Fibre: 10g Calories: 235

Aubergine Pâté

Serves 4

2 large aubergines
2 tbsp olive oil
1 tbsp lemon juice
1 clove garlic, crushed
3 tbsp tahini (sesame seed paste)
½ tsp chilli seasoning
chopped parsley, to garnish
lettuce leaves, cucumber sticks and cauliflower florets, to serve
8 Ryvita mixed varieties crispbreads, to serve

1. Prick aubergines with a fork, place on a baking tray and bake at 180°C/350°F/Gas 4 for 30 minutes or until tender. Cut in half and place the flesh in a food processor.

2. Add olive oil, lemon juice, garlic, tahini and chilli and process to a purée. Leave to cool. Chill.

3. Arrange cucumber sticks and cauliflower florets on lettuce leaves, sprinkle pâté with parsley and serve with Ryvita crispbreads.

Per serving: Fat: 9g Fibre: 7g Calories: 200

Bean and Spinach Salad

Serves 4

225g (8oz) French beans, trimmed
400g (14oz) can red kidney beans, drained
225g (8oz) can chick peas, drained
1 small onion, thinly sliced
4 tbsp olive oil
2 tbsp red wine vinegar
1 tbsp fresh chopped basil
salt and pepper
2 carrots, peeled and grated
3 celery sticks, sliced
225g (8oz) young spinach leaves
8 Ryvita Oat Bran crispbreads
100g (4oz) cottage cheese with chives

1. Cook the French beans in boiling water until just tender. Drain and refresh under cold running water. Mix with red kidney beans, chick peas and onion.

2. Blend oil, vinegar, basil and seasoning together. Add half to bean mixture, toss and leave to marinate for 30 minutes. Add carrots and celery.

3. Arrange spinach leaves in a serving dish. Arrange bean mixture on top, sprinkle with remaining dressing and serve with Ryvita Oat Bran crispbreads topped with cottage cheese.

Per serving: Fat: 15g Fibre: 18g Calories: 395

Special Chicken Salad

Serves 4

1 small lollo rosso lettuce
1 bunch watercress
450g (1lb) cooked chicken, cut into chunks
1 mango, peeled and stoned, cubed
4 spring onions, chopped
25g (1oz) pine nuts, toasted
100g (4oz) strained Greek style yogurt
1 tsp curry paste
2 tbsp mango chutney
4 Ryvita Original crispbreads
50g (2oz) low calorie garlic and herb cheese

1. Arrange lettuce leaves and watercress in a bowl. Add chicken, mango, and spring onions and toss together. Top with pine nuts.

2. Mix yogurt, curry paste and chutney together. Drizzle a little over salad and serve remaining separately.

3. Spread Ryvita Original crispbreads with garlic and herb cheese and serve with salad.

Per serving: Fat: 8·5g Fibre: 5g Calories: 350

Plaice Parcels

Serves 4

4 x 100g (4oz) plaice fillets, skinned
3 sticks celery, sliced
175g (6oz) fine asparagus spears, halved
1 large carrot, cut into matchstick strips
salt and freshly ground black pepper
4 tbsp lemon juice
1 tbsp chopped fresh dill
4 Ryvita Dark Rye crispbreads
50g (2oz) low fat soft cheese with walnuts
lemon wedges, to serve

1. Place fish fillets on four sheets of greaseproof paper. Divide vegetables between fish fillets. Season and top with lemon juice and dill.

2. Fold over greaseproof and seal edges tightly. Place in a roasting tin and cook in a preheated oven at 180°C/350°F/Gas 4 for 20 minutes, until fish and vegetables are tender.

3. Spread Ryvita Dark Rye crispbreads with soft cheese. Serve with fish garnished with lemon wedges.

Per serving: Fat: 4g Fibre: 3·5g Calories: 160

Chinese Style Liver

Serves 4

2 tbsp sesame oil
5 cm (2 in) piece fresh root ginger, grated
2 cloves garlic, crushed
325g (12oz) lamb's liver, cut into thin strips
100g (4oz) courgettes, cut into thin strips
100g (4oz) mangetout, trimmed
75g (3oz) chestnut mushrooms, halved
100g (4oz) carrots, cut into thin strips
2 tbsp light soy sauce
3 tbsp oyster sauce
50g (2oz) cashew nuts
1 tbsp sesame seeds, toasted

1. Heat the oil in a wok or large frying pan, add the ginger and garlic and fry quickly. Add the liver and stir fry for 2-3 minutes.

2. Add the courgettes, mangetout, mushrooms and carrots and stir fry for 3-4 minutes. Mix the soy sauce and oyster sauce together. Add with the cashew nuts and cook for 1 minute.

3. Serve sprinkled with sesame seeds.

Per serving: Fat: 20g Fibre: 5·5g Calories:354

Burgers with Cucumber Relish

Serves 4

8 Ryvita Sesame crispbreads
450g (1lb) lean minced steak
1 onion, grated
1 tbsp tomato purée
freshly ground black pepper
40g (1½oz) low fat soft cheese with garlic and herbs
2 tomatoes, sliced
100g (4oz) cucumber, diced
2 spring onions, chopped
2 tsp chopped fresh mint
110g (4oz) strained Greek style yogurt
gherkins and salad, to garnish

1. Crush 4 Ryvita Sesame crispbreads. Mix with the steak, onion, tomato purée and pepper. Divide into four and shape into burgers.

2. Place on a grill rack, lined with foil and cook for 4-6 minutes per side according to taste. Meanwhile top remaining Ryvita Sesame crispbreads with garlic and herb cheese and tomatoes.

3. Dry cucumber on kitchen paper and mix with spring onions, mint and yogurt. Serve burgers on top of crispbreads, garnished with gherkins. Serve with cucumber relish and salad.

Per serving: Fat: 10g Fibre: 4g Calories: 365

Nutty Vegetable Crumble

Serves 4

450g (1lb) cauliflower florets
225g (8oz) carrots, sliced
225g (8oz) Jerusalem artichokes, peeled and diced
25g (1oz) polyunsaturated margarine
25g (1oz) wholemeal flour
300 ml (½ pt) vegetable stock
200g (7oz) can sweetcorn kernels with peppers
2 tbsp chopped fresh parsley
salt and freshly ground black pepper
6 Ryvita Oat Bran crispbreads, coarsely crushed
3 tbsp sunflower oil
50g (2oz) porridge oats
50g (2oz) mixed nuts, chopped
25g (1oz) Parmesan cheese, grated

1. Place the cauliflower, carrots and artichokes in a pan of boiling water and cook for 7-10 minutes until just tender.

2. Melt the margarine in a pan, and stir in the flour. Gradually add the stock and bring to the boil stirring continuously. Stir in cooked vegetables, sweetcorn, parsley and seasoning. Place in an oven-proof dish.

3. Mix Ryvita, oil, oats, nuts and cheese. Spoon over vegetables and place in a preheated oven at 200°C/400°F/Gas 6 for 15-20 minutes, to brown.

Per serving: Fat: 22g
Fibre: 8·5g
Calories: 320

Herb Baked Halibut

Serves 4

4 x 150g (5oz) halibut or haddock steaks
1 egg, lightly beaten
50g (2oz) fresh breadcrumbs
1 tbsp each chopped fresh chervil, dill and
parsley
salt and freshly ground black pepper
1 tbsp sunflower oil
15g (½oz) butter, melted
225g (8oz) fennel, sliced thinly
225g (8oz) courgettes
2 tbsp lemon juice
lemon wedges, to garnish

1. Dip fish into egg. Mix breadcrumbs, herbs and seasoning together. Dip fish into breadcrumbs to coat.

2. Place fish on a baking tray. Mix oil and butter together and drizzle over. Bake in a preheated oven at 220°C/425°F/Gas 7 for 15 minutes, or until golden.

3. Meanwhile place fennel and courgettes in a pan of boiling water with the lemon juice, and cook until just tender. Serve fish with vegetables, garnished with lemon.

Per serving: Fat: 11g Fibre: 2·5g Calories: 305

Chicken Couscous

Serves 4

350g (12oz) couscous
575g (1¼lb) chicken fillets, diced
1 tbsp olive oil
2 onions, chopped
1 clove garlic, crushed
400g (14oz) can chopped tomatoes
225g (8oz) button mushrooms
1 tsp ground coriander
600 ml (1 pt) chicken stock
salt and freshly ground black pepper
175g (6oz) frozen peas
15g (½oz) butter

1. Soak couscous in 600 ml (1 pt) hot water for 10 minutes. Brown chicken in oil in a large saucepan. Add the onions and garlic and sauté for 2-3 minutes.

2. Add tomatoes, mushrooms, coriander, stock and seasoning and bring to the boil. Place couscous in a sieve or muslin lined steamer, place over meat sauce, cover and simmer for 30 minutes, or until soft.

3. Add peas to meat sauce and cook for 5 minutes. Meanwhile mix couscous with butter and stir until each grain is separate. Serve chicken on a bed of couscous.

Per serving: Fat: 10g Fibre: 7·5g Calories: 400

Fruit Stuffed Pork

Serves 4

900g (2lb) boneless pork loin trimmed of
excess fat, rolled and tied
8 stoned prunes
1 tbsp French mustard
2 tbsp clear honey
350g (12oz) cooking apples, peeled, cored
and sliced
15g (½oz) butter

1. Make a large hole through the pork loin
lengthways, using the handle of a spoon or
similar object. Fill hole with prunes. Place in
a roasting tin.

2. Cook in a preheated oven at 180°C/350°F/
Gas 4 for 1 hour. Mix mustard and 1 tbsp
honey together and brush over meat. Cook
for a further 30 minutes.

3. Meanwhile cook apples with 2 tbsp water
until soft. Beat to pulp with butter and
remaining honey. Serve pork sliced with
apple sauce.

Per serving: Fat: 13g Fibre: 4·5g Calories: 500

Sweet and Sour Vegetables

Serves 4

225g (8oz) can pineapple pieces in fruit juice
1 tsp cornflour
2 tbsp wine vinegar
1 tbsp tomato purée
2 tbsp light muscovado sugar
2 tbsp sunflower oil
2 cloves garlic, crushed
1 onion, sliced
225g (8oz) cauliflower florets
1 carrot, sliced
100g (4oz) young leaf spinach
200g (7oz) can sweetcorn kernels
salt and freshly ground black pepper
225g (8oz) long grain brown rice, cooked,
to serve

1. Drain the pineapple, reserving the juice.
In a small saucepan blend cornflour with
pineapple juice, vinegar, tomato purée and
sugar. Chop the pineapple.

2. Heat the oil in a large frying pan, add the
garlic, onion, cauliflower and carrot and stir
fry over a medium heat for 3-4 minutes. Add
the spinach, chopped pineapple and
sweetcorn and cook for 1-2 minutes.

3. Meanwhile heat the sauce, stirring until
thickened. Season. Serve the vegetables on a
bed of rice, topped with sweet and sour
sauce.

Per serving: Fat: 7g Fibre: 9g Calories: 375

Blushed Cod Steaks

Serves 4

4 x 125g (4oz) cod steaks
300 ml (½ pt) dry white wine or fish stock
salt and freshly ground black pepper
300 ml (½ pt) vegetable stock
3 tbsp lemon juice
1 tbsp cornflour
1 egg
1 tsp mustard powder
1 tbsp tomato purée
½ red pepper, diced
2 tbsp crème fraîche
1 tbsp chopped fresh dill

1. Place the cod steaks in a deep frying pan with the wine or stock and seasoning. Cover and simmer for 7-10 minutes or until fish is tender.

2. Meanwhile mix vegetable stock, lemon juice and cornflour together. Add the egg, mustard powder, tomato purée and pepper. Transfer fish to a warmed serving plate. Add sauce ingredients to pan and stir until thickened but do not boil.

3. Season to taste, stir in crème fraîche and dill and serve with cod steaks.

Per serving: Fat: 5g Fibre: 0·5g Calories: 135

Spinach and Ricotta Flan

Serves 4

75g (3oz) plain flour
4 Ryvita Original crispbreads, crushed
50g (2oz) polyunsaturated margarine
450g (1lb) young leaf spinach, cooked until just tender
225g (8oz) ricotta cheese
2 eggs, lightly beaten
½ tsp ground nutmeg
salt and freshly ground black pepper
25g (1oz) mature Cheddar cheese, grated

1. Mix flour and crispbreads together in a food processor. Add margarine and process to form fine breadcrumbs. Add 2-3 tbsp cold water and mix to a dough. Wrap and chill for 30 minutes.

2. Roll out pastry and use to line a 20 cm (8 in) flan ring. Drain any excess moisture from spinach and chop. Spread over pastry base.

3. Beat cheese, eggs, nutmeg and seasoning together and pour over spinach. Sprinkle with Cheddar cheese.

4. Bake in a preheated oven 190°C/375°F/ Gas 5 for 45 minutes, until set and golden.

Per serving: Fat: 57g Fibre: 9g Calories: 435

Spicy Beef Bake

Serves 4

1 tbsp vegetable oil
2 onions, chopped
1 carrot, chopped
1 stick celery, chopped
550g (1¼lb) lean minced beef
1 tbsp tomato purée
400g (14oz) can chopped tomatoes
1 tsp curry paste
salt and freshly ground black pepper
225g (8oz) potatoes, sliced
1 tbsp cornflour
225g (8oz) strained Greek style yogurt
2 eggs, lightly beaten

1. Heat the oil in a large pan, add the onions, carrot and celery and fry for 5 minutes. Add beef and fry until browned.

2. Stir in the tomato purée, tomatoes, curry paste and seasoning. Bring to the boil, cover and simmer for 15 minutes. Meanwhile cook potatoes in a lightly salted boiling water for 5 minutes. Drain and cool.

3. Place half the beef mix in an oven-proof dish, top with potatoes and remaining beef. Mix cornflour, yogurt and eggs together. Season and pour over. Cook in a preheated oven at 180°C/350°F/Gas 4 for 45-50 minutes until set.

Per serving: Fat:19g Fibre:3·5g
Calories: 425

Chicken and Pasta Pot

Serves 4

2 tbsp sunflower oil
2 red onions, sliced
450g (1lb) diced chicken
600 ml (1pt) chicken or vegetable stock
100g (4oz) wholemeal pasta shapes
3 courgettes, cut into chunks
175g (6oz) button mushrooms, halved
1 red pepper, diced
100g (4oz) frozen peas
2 tbsp chopped fresh tarragon
salt and freshly ground black pepper

1. Heat the oil in a large pan, add the onions and fry for 3-4 minutes. Add the chicken and brown on all sides.

2. Add the stock and bring to the boil. Add the pasta, courgettes, mushrooms and pepper and cook for 10 minutes. Add peas and cook for 3-4 minutes, or until pasta is tender.

3. Add tarragon, season to taste and serve.

Per serving: Fat 10g Fibre: 8g Calories: 310

Seafood Cheese Platter

Serves 4

1 small cooking apple, peeled and cored
225g (8oz) Chèvre, cut into 4 slices
2 tbsp single cream
4 Ryvita Dark Rye crispbreads
4 tsp pesto sauce
100g (4oz) smoked salmon, torn into strips
1 small ripe avocado, peeled and sliced
2 tbsp reduced calorie mayonnaise
juice and zest 2 limes
dash Tabasco
salad leaves, to garnish

1. Cut apple into four, horizontally, and top with cheese. Place on a baking tray, drizzle over cream. Bake in a preheated oven at 200°C/400°F/Gas 6 for 8-10 minutes.

2. Meanwhile spread Ryvita Dark Rye crispbreads with pesto sauce. Arrange salmon and avocado on four serving plates. Mix mayonnaise, lime juice and Tabasco together.

3. Place cheese rounds on top of crispbreads. Place on serving plates, garnish with salad leaves, drizzle sauce over avocado and top with lime zest.

Per serving: Fat: 29g Fibre: 4g Calories: 380

Lamb with Lemon Sauce

Serves 4

8 lamb cutlets, trimmed of excess fat
2 tbsp sunflower oil
1 onion, chopped
1 clove garlic, crushed
100g (4oz) no need to soak apricots, halved
2 tsp chopped fresh thyme
250 ml (8 floz) dry white wine
salt and freshly ground black pepper
225g (8oz) can chick peas, drained
grated rind and juice 2 lemons
2 egg yolks
thyme sprigs, to garnish

1. Brown cutlets in oil in a large pan. Remove. Add onion and garlic and cook for 4-5 minutes. Stir in apricots, thyme, wine and seasoning. Add cutlets, cover and simmer gently for 40 minutes.

2. Add chick peas and cook for 5 minutes. Mix lemon rind and juice with egg yolks. Add 3 tbsp liquid from the pan, then stir this into the sauce in the pan.

3. Cook gently for 1 minute, stirring. Do not boil. Serve cutlets with sauce, garnished with sprigs of thyme.

Per serving: Fat: 22g Fibre: 11g Calories: 450

Venison with Port

Serves 4

4 x 100g (4oz) venison steaks
150 ml (¼ pt) Port
3 tbsp red wine vinegar
2 tbsp olive oil
2 bay leaves
4 sprigs thyme
1 onion, chopped
1 carrot, sliced
175g (6oz) button mushrooms, sliced
1 tbsp wholemeal flour
150 ml (5 floz) vegetable stock
2 tsp wholegrain mustard
salt and freshly ground black pepper

1. Place venison in a dish. Mix port, vinegar, 1 tbsp oil, bay leaves and thyme together. Pour over, cover and leave to marinade overnight in a cool place.

2. Heat remaining oil. Remove steaks from marinade and brown. Remove. Add onion, carrot and mushrooms and cook for 5 minutes.

3. Stir in the flour, then gradually add the marinade and stock. Bring to the boil, stirring continuously.

4. Add the steaks, cover and simmer for 30 minutes. Remove bay leaves and thyme. Stir in mustard, season to taste and serve.

Per serving: Fat: 8g Fibre: 10g
Calories: 310

Chicken and Ham Bundles

Serves 4

75g (3oz) feta cheese
4 x 75g (3oz) cooked chicken breast fillets
4 thin slices Parma ham
freshly ground black pepper
4 large sheets filo pastry, halved
50g (2oz) butter, melted
lettuce and tomatoes, to garnish

1. Place slices of cheese on top of chicken. Wrap in a piece of ham and season with pepper.

2. Brush filo pastry with butter and arrange into four piles of two, displacing the second sheet a quarter of a turn. Place chicken on top. Lift pastry edges and pinch together to form a bundle.

3. Place on a baking sheet, brush with remaining butter and bake in a preheated oven at 180°C/350°F/Gas 4 for 20-30 minutes until golden.

Per serving: Fat: 15g Fibre: 1·5g Calories: 270

Summer Fish Ring

Serves 4

225g (8oz) long grain brown rice
½ red pepper, finely chopped
50g (2oz) peanuts
75g (3oz) frozen peas
100g (4oz) sweetcorn kernels
2 tbsp oil free French dressing
salt and freshly ground black pepper
3 tbsp strained Greek style yogurt
1-2 tbsp tomato purée
198g (7oz) can tuna in brine
225g (8oz) peeled prawns
175g (6oz) shelled mussels
salad leaves

1. Cook rice in a large pan of boiling salted water for 30 minutes or until just tender. Drain. Rinse in cold water and drain again. Mix with pepper, peanuts, peas, sweetcorn, dressing and seasoning.

2. Press into a lightly oiled 1 litre (1¾ pt) ring mould and chill. Mix yogurt, tomato purée and seasoning together. Add tuna, prawns and mussels.

3. To serve, turn rice ring on to a serving plate. Fill centre with salad leaves and fish. Serve.

Per serving: Fat: 4g Fibre: 7g Calories: 450

Turkey Nicoise

Serves 4

4 x 100g (4oz) turkey breast fillets
2 tbsp Dijon mustard
2 tbsp clear honey
1 tbsp lemon juice
salt and freshly ground black pepper
4 tomatoes, cut into wedges
225g (8oz) French beans, cooked
1 egg, hard boiled, shelled and quartered
50g (2oz) stoned black olives
½ cucumber, sliced
4 tbsp French dressing
12 anchovies, halved lengthways

1. Place the turkey on a lightly oiled baking tray, cover with foil and cook in a preheated oven at 200°C/400°F/Gas 6 for 20 minutes. Meanwhile mix mustard, honey, lemon juice and seasoning together.

2. Remove foil from turkey, brush with mustard mix and cook for a further 10 minutes. Leave to cool. Arrange tomatoes, beans, egg, olives and cucumber on a serving plate. Pour over the dressing and leave for 30 minutes.

3. Decorate with anchovies, top with turkey and serve.

Per serving: Fat: 12g Fibre: 4g Calories: 310

Spinach and Ham Frittata

Serves 4

75g (3oz) wholewheat spaghetti
salt and freshly ground black pepper
1 tbsp olive oil
1 onion, chopped
2 celery sticks, chopped
100g (4oz) young leaf spinach
5 eggs
150 ml (5 floz) skimmed milk
1 tsp dried oregano
50g (2oz) ham, cut into thin strips
25g (1oz) pine nuts

1. Place the spaghetti in a large pan of boiling lightly salted water and cook for 10 minutes until just tender. Drain. Meanwhile heat the oil in a large heavy based frying pan and fry the onion and celery.

2. Add the spinach and cook for 2 minutes. Mix the eggs, milk, oregano, seasoning, ham, pine nuts and spaghetti together. Pour into the pan and cook over a low heat for 5 minutes, stirring occasionally.

3. Cook for a further 10 minutes until underside is browned and centre is set. Place under a preheated grill to brown. Serve cut into wedges.

Per serving: Fat: 15g Fibre: 6g Calories: 300

Salmon with Watercress

Serves 4

4 salmon steaks
125 ml (4 floz) dry white wine
175 ml (6 floz) vegetable stock
1 onion, chopped
2 bay leaves
1 bunch watercress
25g (1oz) plain flour blended with
25g (1oz) polyunsaturated margarine
3 tbsp crème fraîche
salt and freshly ground black pepper
150g (6oz) broccoli florets, cooked

1. Place the salmon in a large frying pan, add the wine, stock, onion and bay leaves and bring to the boil. Cover and simmer for 7-10 minutes, until cooked. Meanwhile remove coarse stalks from watercress and chop remainder.

2. Transfer salmon to warmed serving plates and keep warm. Remove bay leaves from sauce, add watercress and flour and margarine mix. Stir until thickened.

3. Purée sauce in a blender or food processor. Stir in crème fraîche and seasoning. Add a little extra stock, if too thick. Reheat gently. Serve sauce with salmon steaks, garnished with broccoli.

Per serving: Fat:19g Fibre: 3·5g Calories: 335

Apricot and Orange Ripple

Serves 4

100g (4oz) no need to soak apricots
250 ml (8 floz) orange juice
150g (5oz) strained Greek style yogurt
150g (5oz) low fat natural yogurt
310g (11oz) can mandarin oranges in fruit juice, drained

1. Place the apricots and orange juice in a pan and bring to the boil. Simmer for 15 minutes or until tender. Leave to cool then purée in a food processor or blender.

2. Mix yogurts together. Ripple the apricot purée through the yogurt.

3. Place mandarin oranges in the base of four glasses. Pour over ripple mix and serve.

Per serving: Fat: 5g Fibre: 7g Calories: 165

Apple and Raspberry Crumble

Serves 4

450g (1lb) tart eating apples, peeled, cored and sliced
1 tbsp lemon juice
½ tsp ground nutmeg
225g (8oz) fresh or defrosted frozen raspberries
50g (2oz) sultanas
2 tbsp honey
100g (4oz) muesli
1 tbsp muscovado sugar
25g (1oz) polyunsaturated margarine, melted
½ tsp ground cinnamon

1. Mix apples with lemon juice and nutmeg. Stir in raspberries, sultanas and honey. Place in a shallow oven-proof dish.

2. Mix muesli and sugar together. Stir in margarine and cinnamon. Sprinkle over fruit and bake at 190°C/375°F/Gas 5 for 20-25 minutes.

Per serving: Fat: 23g Fibre: 10g Calories: 280

Fruit Baskets

Serves 4

300 ml (½ pt) red grape juice
2 tsp arrowroot
200g (7oz) low calorie apricot fromage frais
4 brandy snap baskets
175g (6oz) red seedless grapes
175g (6oz) strawberries, halved
1 large banana, sliced
1 star fruit, sliced
6 tsp soured cream

1. Mix grape juice and arrowroot together. Bring to the boil, stirring until thickened. Cover and leave to cool.

2. Divide fromage frais between brandy baskets. Mix grapes, strawberries, banana, and star fruit together and arrange on top of fromage frais.

3. Pour sauce onto four serving plates. Marble soured cream through sauce. Place brandy baskets in the centre and serve.

Per serving: Fat: 5g Fibre: 2·5g Calories: 220

Curd Tart

Serves 6

75g (3oz) plain flour
4 Ryvita Original crispbreads, finely crushed
50g (2oz) polyunsaturated margarine
75g (3oz) curd cheese
75g (3oz) cottage cheese
2 eggs, lightly beaten
25g (1oz) sultanas
25g (1oz) dried pears, chopped
25g (1oz) walnuts, chopped
grated rind ½ lemon
40g (1½oz) muscovado sugar

1. Mix flour and Ryvita Original crispbreads together. Rub in margarine until it resembles fine breadcrumbs. Add 1-2 tbsp cold water and mix to a dough. Wrap and chill for 30 minutes.

2. Roll out pastry and use to line an 18 cm (7 in) fluted flan ring. Sieve cheeses into a bowl, beat in eggs, sultanas, pears, walnuts, lemon rind and sugar. Pour into pastry case.

3. Bake in a preheated oven at 190°C/375°F/ Gas 5 for 30 minutes. Reduce to 180°C/ 350°F/Gas 4 for 20 minutes, until set and golden.

Per serving: Fat: 32g Fibre: 3·5g Calories: 285

Speedy Trifle

Serves 6

175g (6oz) trifle sponge cakes
2 tbsp apricot conserve
4 tbsp sherry
2 tbsp apple juice
2 apples, cored and chopped
2 bananas, sliced
225g (8oz) fresh or defrosted frozen
raspberries
425g (15oz) can low fat custard, chilled
250g (9oz) strained Greek style yogurt,
chilled
25g (1oz) toasted flaked almonds
raspberries or banana slices, to decorate

1. Spread sponge with apricot conserve and cut into cubes. Place in the base of a trifle dish. Sprinkle with sherry.

2. Toss apples and bananas in apple juice, mix with raspberries and place on top of sponge.

3. Top with custard and yogurt. Sprinkle with almonds, decorate with fruit and serve.

Per serving: Fat: 7g Fibre: 6g Calories: 300

Citrus Delight

Serves 4

1 x 10·5g sachet sugar free lemon jelly
175g (6oz) fresh fruit, chopped if large
2 eggs, separated
40g (1½oz) caster sugar
juice 2 oranges
2 tsp powdered gelatine
150g (5oz) strained Greek style yogurt

1. Dissolve lemon jelly in 300 ml (½ pt) boiling water. Make up to 450 ml (¾ pt) with cold water. Divide between four tall glasses, add fruit and refrigerate to set.

2. Whisk egg yolks and sugar together until thick and creamy, using an electric mixer. Gradually whisk in orange juice. Sprinkle gelatine over 2 tbsp cold water in a small bowl. Leave for 5 minutes, then stand in a pan of hot water and stir until dissolved. Stir into egg mix.

3. Chill until beginning to set. Fold in yogurt. Whisk egg whites until stiff and fold in. Divide between glasses and chill until set.

Per serving: Fat: 6·5g Fibre: 1g Calories: 160

Cheesecake

Serves 6

*80g (3oz) wholemeal digestive biscuits,
crushed
6 Ryvita Original crispbreads, crushed
25g (1oz) hazelnuts, ground
50g (2oz) polyunsaturated margarine,
melted
3 tsp powdered gelatine
2 tbsp lemon juice
225g (8oz) cottage cheese, sieved
150 ml (5·floz) soured cream
150 ml (5 floz) natural yogurt
50g (2oz) caster sugar
2 egg whites
fresh fruit, to decorate*

1. Mix biscuits, crispbreads, nuts and
margarine together. Press into the base of a
20 cm (8 in) loose bottomed cake tin. Chill.

2. Sprinkle the gelatine over the lemon juice
in a small bowl. Stand in a pan of hot water
and stir until dissolved. Mix cottage cheese,
cream, yogurt, sugar and gelatine together.

3. Whisk egg whites until stiff then fold into
cheesecake mix. Pour into tin and chill until
set. To serve, remove from tin and decorate
with fruit.

Per serving: Fat: 18g Fibre: 2·3g Calories: 285

Mixed Fruit Brulée

Serves 4

*450g (1lb) frozen mixed summer fruits
2 tsp cornflour
8 tsp demerara sugar
225g (8oz) strained Greek style yogurt,
chilled*

1. Place the fruit in a saucepan and slowly
bring to the boil. Cook for 5 minutes or until
tender. Mix cornflour with 2 tbsp water and
4 tsp sugar. Stir into fruit. Stir until
thickened.

2. Divide between four individual heat-proof
dishes and leave until cold. Top with yogurt
and sprinkle with sugar. Place under a
preheated grill until sugar melts.

Per serving: Fat: 5g Fibre: 3·5g Calories: 145

Kir Spritzer Royale

Serves 1

1 tsp Crème de Cassis
75 ml (3 floz) dry white wine, chilled
75 ml (3 floz) sparkling mineral water,
chilled

1. Place the Crème de Cassis and dry white wine in a wine glass and stir to mix. Top up with sparkling mineral water and serve.

(75 calories per serving)

Iced Citrus Coffee

Serves 1

150 ml (¼ pt) strong black coffee, chilled
75 ml (3 floz) skimmed milk, chilled
1 tbsp vanilla ice cream
2 tbsp fresh orange juice, chilled
artificial sweetener, to taste
orange peel, to decorate

1. Whisk coffee, milk, ice cream and orange juice together. Sweeten to taste and serve decorated with orange peel.

(65 calories per serving)

Citrus Punch

Serves 4

juice 2 limes
juice 2 grapefruits
150 ml (¼ pt) orange juice, chilled
600 ml (1 pt) low calorie lemonade
lime slices, to decorate

1. Strain the lime and grapefruit juices into a jug, add the orange juice and top up with lemonade. Serve decorated with lime slices.

(20 calories per serving)

Warming Honey Cup

Serves 2

450 ml (¾ pt) apple juice
1 tbsp clear honey
¼ tsp ground ginger
¼ tsp ground nutmeg
1 stick cinnamon
2 tbsp lemon juice
apple slices, to decorate

1. Place all the ingredients except apple slices in a pan and slowly bring to the boil, stirring occasionally. Serve decorated with apple slices.

(105 calories per serving)

Tomato Cocktail

Serves 1

225g (8oz) ripe tomatoes, chopped
½ small onion, finely chopped
1 tsp Worcestershire sauce
1 carrot, chopped
juice of 2 oranges
mint sprig to decorate, optional

1. Place the tomatoes, onion, Worcestershire sauce, carrot and orange juice in a food processor and liquidise. Strain into a glass and serve decorated with a sprig of mint.

(65 calories per serving)

Fruit Cup Sparkle

Serves 4

300 ml (½ pt) mandarin juice, chilled
300 ml (½ pt) pineapple juice, chilled
300 ml (½ pt) low calorie ginger ale, chilled
pineapple wedges, to decorate

1. Mix the fruit juices together. Top up with ginger ale and serve decorated with pieces of fresh or tinned pineapple.

(65 calories per serving)

Thick Strawberry Shake

Serves 1

75g (3oz) strawberries
100g (4oz) pot low calorie fromage frais
2 tbsp low fat natural yogurt
50 ml (2 floz) skimmed milk
1 strawberry, halved, to decorate

1. Place strawberries, fromage frais, yogurt and milk in a food processor and liquidise. Serve decorated with a fresh strawberry.

(110 calories per serving)

Bedtime Toddy

Serves 2

1 egg
2 tsp light muscovado sugar
2 tbsp brandy or rum
300 ml (½ pt) skimmed milk
grated nutmeg

1. Whisk the egg, sugar and brandy together. Heat the milk until almost boiling. Pour onto egg mixture and whisk together. Serve topped with nutmeg.

(135 calories per serving)

Ryvita Survival Tips

However hard you try to stick to a diet, there are times when you just crave for something extra, or a special treat. Don't give up, indulge yourself in one or two of the following.

Either balance your calorie count by choosing lower calorie dishes for the rest of your days allowance or omit a snack or dessert the following day.

Tempted to have a glass of wine with a special meal. Allow 100 calories from your daily allowance for a 140 ml (5 floz) glass of dry white wine.

Eat an orange or a small banana. (50 calories)

Spread 1 Ryvita Dark Rye crispbread with 1 tbsp low calorie coleslaw and top with a 25g (1oz) slice ham. (65 calories)

For a speedy break have 1 Ryvita Original crispbread spread with 2 tsp low sugar marmalade. (50 calories)

A glass of fruit juice is always welcome. A 140 ml (5 floz) glass of apple, orange or grapefruit is 50 calories.

Try 1 Ryvita Oat Bran crispbread, topped with 1 tbsp cottage cheese and pineapple, sprinkled with 1 tsp chopped almonds. (55 calories)

If you are a chocoholic indulge yourself with a fun sized Mars bar. (85 calories)

Eat 1 Ryvita Sesame crispbread spread with 1 t crab paste, topped with slices of cucumber. (50 calories)

For a tasty snack try 1 Ryvita Original crispbread with 25g (1oz) slice of turkey breast meat and 1 tsp cranberry sauce. (75 calories)

Grapes are easy to eat and digest. 110g (4oz) bunch is around 60 calories.

74

A 280 ml (½ pt) glass of lager will add 90 calories, whilst alcohol free lager is only 50 calories.

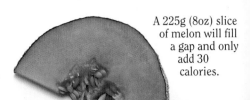

A 225g (8oz) slice of melon will fill a gap and only add 30 calories.

Eat a Ryvita Oat Bran crispbread topped with 1 tsp marmite and a few slices of tomato. (50 calories)

Nibble on a carrot, 2 sticks of celery or a 5 cm (2 in) piece of cucumber. (12 calories each)

Try 3 tbsp low fat natural yogurt mixed with 50g (2oz) diced cucumber and 1 tsp chopped mint. Eat with 1 Ryvita Dark Rye crispbread and 2 cherry tomatoes. (70 calories)

1 Ryvita Dark Rye crispbread, topped with 2 chopped crab sticks mixed with 1 tsp low calorie mayonnaise. (70 calories)

Drink lots of mineral water; it will help to keep the hunger pangs away without adding calories.

For a savoury nibble eat 1 Ryvita Original crispbread spread with 15g (½ oz) low fat garlic and herb cheese, garnished with 1 sliced stuffed olive. (50 calories)

Try 1 Ryvita Sesame crispbread spread with 2 tsp low fat sugar jam, topped with 2 sliced strawberries. (55 calories)

Ingredients File

The range of foods readily available has grown dramatically in recent years. Many more fresh fruits, vegetables and herbs are available; as well as low fat, reduced sugar and high fibre foods.

Now you are looking at a healthier lifestyle it is important to cook recipes which are suitable. The following pages show both familiar and unusual ingredients which have been used in this book, and which can be used in your own meals.

The sections on cheese and milk, cream and yogurt provide lots of lower fat alternatives to higher calorie products, which you may have been using.

The fruit and vegetable sections endorses the importance of including lots of these high fibre, low calorie foods. Fresh fruit and vegetables provide many of the vitamins and minerals essential for healthy living.

The large number of fresh herbs and dried spices readily available in the shops, enables you to add interest and variety to your diet without adding calories. Herbs contain less than 1 calorie per 5 ml (tsp) whilst spices vary from less than 1 to around 8 calories per 5 ml (tsp).

The section on sugar provides information on alternative sweeteners to white sugar, whilst the page on breads and crispbreads offer some guidance on selecting these foods.

Use these pages for reference, to help you provide a more varied diet for both your family and yourself.

Milk, cream and yogurt

Milk products have been an extremely important source of food for centuries. They are regarded as one of the most important sources of calcium. However, they are also high in saturated fats, and in general, our intake is higher than is good for us. To this end a number of alternatives are now readily available in the supermarkets. These products are lower in saturated fats and of course lower in calories. In addition to these products there are also lower calorie versions of double and single cream.

Buttermilk - The by-product of butter making. Similar to milk, but with less fat (only about 0·5%) and vitamin A.

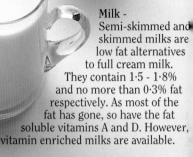

Milk - Semi-skimmed and skimmed milks are low fat alternatives to full cream milk. They contain 1·5 - 1·8% and no more than 0·3% fat respectively. As most of the fat has gone, so have the fat soluble vitamins A and D. However, vitamin enriched milks are available.

Yogurt, low fat - made from concentrated skimmed milk, low fat yogurt has around 0·5 - 2·0% fat. Yogurt is an excellent source of calcium and protein.

Greek-style Yogurt - A high fat yogurt between 6 - 10% but still lower in fat than single cream. It is rich and creamy and the higher fat content helps to neutralise the acidity.

Smetana/smatana - Made from skimmed milk and cream. It is a good low fat substitute for cream in cooking. Add towards the end of cooking and do not boil, for it will curdle.

Soured cream - A pasteurized cream with an added souring culture. It has the same fat content as single cream. Use to enrich casseroles, soups, as a basis for a dip or on baked potatoes.

Crème Fraîche - A French soured cream. It is lightly acidic without being sour. Lower in calories than double cream. It is delicious with fruit.

Cheese

Cheese is a good source of complete protein, vitamins and minerals, and is available in so many types and flavours that it is a universally eaten food product. However, many cheeses contain a high level of saturated fat which means their consumption needs to be limited. Below are examples of lower fat cheeses which are preferable. Their lower fat content also reduces their calorific values.
In addition to these cheeses there are a number of lower fat varieties of high fat cheeses such as Cheddar and Cheshire cheeses now available.

Curd Cheese - A slightly tart cheese with a refreshing flavour. Use it fresh or in cooking. 54 calories per 28g/1oz.

Roquefort - A semi soft crumbly cheese with a green blue marbling. A good low calorie blue cheese. 88 calories per 28g/1oz.

Cottage Cheese - Made from skimmed cows milk which is warmed to form soft lumps. It is then drained and coated with thin cream. It is rich in calcium and vitamin B_2 and B_{12}. It has a clean mild flavour and is available plain or flavoured with herbs, fruit or vegetables. Extra low fat varieties are available. 27 calories per 28g/1oz.

Mozzarella - An Italian unripened cheese. A mild flavour. Traditionally used to top pizza. Around 90 calories per 28g/1oz.

Parmesan - Made from semi-skimmed cows milk. It has a fruity flavour. Whilst higher in calories, its distinctive flavour means you can use less. 118 calories per 28g/1oz

Skimmed milk soft cheese - quark - A fresh curd cheese made from skimmed milk with no salt. It has a delicate sour flavour and a spoonable texture. 20 calories per 28g/1oz.

Edam - A Dutch semi-hard cheese, made from skimmed cows milk. It is relatively low in calories; has a mild nutty flavour and keeps well. 90 calories per 28g/1oz.

Chèvre - A goats cheese with a creamy but tangy flavour. A good source of minerals. Good eaten fresh or cooked. Around 88 calories per 28g/1oz.

Brie - A ripened soft cheese recognisable by its edible outer rind. Avoid cheese with a chalky inside, it is under ripe; or a very runny cheese smelling of ammonia, it is over ripe. 88 calories per 28g/1oz.

Feta - A Greek cheese made from ewes or cows milk. It is preserved in brine, so should be washed before eating. It has a firm crumbly texture, and tastes delicious sprinkled over salads. 85 calories per 28g/1oz.

Ricotta - An Italian unripened whey cheese with a bland slightly sweet flavour. 55 calories per 28g/1oz.

Vegetables

Vegetables are an extremely good source of vitamins and minerals. They also provide plenty of fibre which helps the digestion of other foods. Some vegetables like potatoes and parsnips provide complex carbohydrates which are digested more slowly and therefore are more satisfying for a longer period of time. Vegetables are also low in fat, so provide a good source of low calorie food. Always store in a cool dark place to reduce nutrient loss.

Spinach - An excellent vegetable raw or cooked, providing vitamins A and C as well as calcium. Use in omelettes, salads or with eggs, fish and ham.

Asparagus - A tasty spring and summer vegetable which can be eaten alone or used in soups, stir fries, omelettes and salads. Good source of vitamin E.

Aubergine - Aubergine can be baked, casseroled or stuffed. They have a great affinity for tomatoes. Use with herbs for added flavour.

Leek - A good winter vegetable with a mild oniony flavour. Provides vitamin B_6 and iron. Use in soups, casseroles, stir fries or as a main vegetable.

Peppers - These vegetables are available in a variety of colours. They have a sweet flavour and crunchy texture. Use raw or cooked in salads, sauces, casseroles or stuffed.

Mushrooms - Many types of mushrooms of varying sizes and flavours are available. They are a source of protein, iron, copper, potassium, and vitamins B_1 and B_2. Serve raw or cooked.

Broccoli - A versatile vegetable, for adding to soups, stir fries or to serve with fish or meat. Can be eaten blanched as a crudité. Contains vitamins A, B_2, C and folic acid.

Red Cabbage - A crunchy vegetable which is delicious raw in salads. Contains vitamin C, folic acid and potassium.

Tomato - An extremely versatile ingredient which can be used raw or cooked in soups, sauces, casseroles, with pasta, meat or fish and in salads. Rich in vitamins B_2, C, potassium and phosphorus.

Corn Cob - Best eaten very fresh. It provides vitamins A and C.

Beetroot - Rich in folic acid and sodium, this vegetable is most commonly served in salads. Can also be used in soup.

Cucumber - A cool flavour ideal in salads, dips, sauces and soups, or as raw sticks to eat between meals.

Watercress - This peppery leaf is a good source of vitamin A, iodine and potassium. Use in salads, soups and sauces or as an edible garnish.

Bean-sprouts- Bean-sprouts can be eaten raw in salads or cooked in stir fries. They are a rich source of A and B vitamins.

Fruit

Fruits provide a source of energy because they contain fruit sugar. They are rich in fibre both in the edible skin and in certain fruits, such as apples, in water soluble fibre called pectin.

Dried fruits are very high in fibre. Fresh fruit is a good source of vitamins and minerals especially vitamin C, and most fruits are low in calories.

Melon - A wide variety of melons are available. They are low in calories and are delicious on their own, for breakfast; combined with other fresh fruits, cold meats or shellfish.

Mango - A versatile fruit suited to both sweet and savoury dishes. A good source of vitamins A and C.

Peaches - Eat raw or gently poached. A useful source of vitamins A and C.

Strawberries - Almost everyones favourite fruit; low in calories, rich in flavour and a useful source of vitamin C.

Kiwi - An extremely good source of vitamin C. One of these sweet but acidic fruits contains more than your daily requirements of vitamin C.

Apricots - Apricots are rich in vitamins A and C and iron. The dried fruits are an excellent source of fibre.

Currants - Redcurrants can be eaten raw or cooked, but blackcurrants are usually too tart and are best eaten cooked. Sweeten with honey or artificial sweetener. Good source of vitamin C.

Blackberries - An excellent autumn fruit rich in vitamin C.

Pineapple - The sweet, fragrant and astringent flavour of pineapple is unique. It is perfect eaten in slices or wedges or with meat or cheese. It is a good source of vitamin C and fibre. It also contains an enzyme which breaks down protein and is therefore an aid to digestion at the end of a rich meal.

Oranges - Oranges like all citrus fruits are a valuable source of vitamin C. Include the grated rind as well as the juice in casseroles and desserts to impart extra flavour.

Bananas - Bananas are delicious raw, baked or flambéed. They can even be cooked on a barbecue. Good source of vitamins A, B_6 and folic acid.

Raspberries - Rich in fibre when eaten whole.

Apples - Apples are a good source of fibre and also provide potassium. Eat complete with skin.

Grapes - Grapes are easy to digest and so provide a good source of fast energy. They also provide potassium.

Spices

Spices, like herbs, add interest to cooking and stimulate the taste buds. Spices ensure that food does not have to be bland to be low in calories. Dried spices are best purchased whole and grated or ground as needed. Ready ground spices, whilst a labour saving alternative, will lose the flavour and scent more quickly, probably within 6 months. Store all spices in airtight glass jars away from heat and light.

Paprika - Made from ground pimiento seeds and varies from mild and sweet to pungent and hot. Particularly good with fish and shellfish as well as meat and poultry.

Ginger - Available fresh and dried. The dramatic flavour of fresh ginger is very different to the dried form. Use fresh ginger for savoury dishes It is excellent in curries and is rich in minerals

Cinnamon - Available as strips of bark or in powdered form. As it is difficult to grind, it is best purchased ground. Used for flavouring when poaching fruits. Use in stick form as a flavouring for casseroles and drinks.

Turmeric - A dried root most commonly bought in powdered form. A slightly musty flavour and woody aroma and is mainly used to add a yellow colouring to curries and rice dishes.

Nutmeg - Available whole or ground. The ground powder deteriorates quickly, so is best when finely grated. It can be used in both sweet and savoury recipes and imparts a warm, sweetish flavour.

Peppercorns - Available as green, black or white. Green peppercorns are the mildest. White peppercorns are hot and less aromatic than black pepper.

Cumin - A distinctive sweetish slightly hot flavour. Use seeds or powdered form; the seeds are more pungent. A versatile spice which can be used with fish, meat or vegetables.

Caraway Seeds - A pungent spice with a taste similar to aniseed and fennel. Delicious with cabbage, pork and in soups.

Coriander - Use the seeds whole or ground in curries, soups and stews. It has a fairly mild flavour which can add a pleasing savoury note to most foods.

Cloves - Cloves contain an aromatic and powerful oil, so use sparingly. Stick whole cloves into onions and cook the onion with meat or infuse in milk for savoury sauces. Use ground cloves to flavour hot spiced drinks and desserts.

Chilli - Available green or red as whole chillies or in powder form. Fresh chillies are very hot, whilst the powdered form comes in varying strengths. Add to stir fries, meat, poultry and egg dishes.

Herbs

Herbs, whilst not important as an everyday source of nutrition, are indispensable to good cooking. They contribute greatly by adding a distinct flavour and character to many recipes. By using herbs you are adding flavour and interest to food without adding lots of calories. Where possible use fresh herbs as many lose their flavour once dried. Some of the more pungent herbs such as sage, bay, rosemary, oregano, marjoram and dill keep well when dried, but must be stored in an airtight container. Dried herbs are more concentrated than fresh ones, so use about half the quantity.

Chives - These slender green spikes are used to impart a mild onion flavour to cheese, egg, poultry and fish dishes. The lilac pink flowers are also edible and are good in salads.

Basil - A warm spicy smell and flavour, similar to cloves. Perfect with tomato dishes and pasta.

Coriander - The leaves are intensely aromatic and are delicious added to salads, or sprinkled over cooked meat, fish and vegetable dishes.

Tarragon - An aromatic herb with a hint of aniseed. Mainly used in soups and salads. Excellent with poultry.

Mint - Available in many varieties such as spearmint, applemint, Bowles mint. A versatile herb used sparingly in both sweet and savoury cooking.

Bay leaf - Long cooking releases the distinct flavour from this herb. Add to stews, casseroles and soups. Add to bouquet garni.

Parsley -
Principle ingredients of bouquet garni
and used in stocks, sauces, stuffings and
fish dishes. Available as English or French
parsley, the French flat leafed variety
having a finer flavour. Both contain iron
and vitamin C.

Dill - A subtle, aniseed
like flavour used as a mild
flavouring for fish, egg,
potato and poultry dishes.
Also added to salads and
salad dressings.

Sage - A very powerful
flavouring, so use sparingly. Delicious with
dairy products; vegetables such as tomatoes,
peas, beans, and meats such as pork, duck
and liver.

Marjoram - Belongs to the same family as
oregano. Both have a powerful flavour, which
remains even after cooking. A traditional
flavouring for pasta, pizza, Greek salads and
poultry.

Thyme -
A popular
herb, used
in bouquet
garni and
ideal with
soups and
pasta.

Sweeteners

Sugar is a cheap energy source, high in calories and low in nourishment. In general our sugar consumption is too high. However, even if we reduce our intake, sweeteners are still likely to form part of our diet, so below is a selection of alternative sweeteners. Some are artificial sweeteners; some are sweeter than refined sugar, so provide less calories, because a smaller amount is used. Some provide the same calories but are less refined; whilst others provide an alternative in the form of fruit sugar or fructose.

To use the energy present in sugar the body requires certain vitamins, especially B_1. This is present in molasses, so molasses enriched sugars at least provide this vitamin.

Apple Juice - Fruit juices such as apple or orange. They can be added to dried or fresh fruit instead of refined sugar.

Dark Muscovado Sugar - Contains around 10% molasses. The higher molasses content gives a stronger, richer taste.

Artificial Granulated Sweeteners - Based on sweeteners such as saccharin or aspartamine are available and provide only about 10% of the calories of sugar. Some sweeteners may leave an unpleasant slightly bitter after taste.

Honey - Whilst honey is virtually pure sugar, it is a natural sweetener, and because it has a strong flavour, less is used to sweeten foods. It contains trace elements.

Treacle or Molasses - The residue from refining cane sugar. It has a strong slightly bitter flavour. Contains some calcium, iron and B vitamins. Ideal with fruit.

Molasses Sugar or Black Barbados Sugar - Contains about 20% molasses. It is the least refined of all cane sugars and so retains the most minerals, particularly calcium and vitamin B_1.

Dried Fruits - Dried fruits such as apricots, pears, peaches, dates and sultanas all add a natural fruit super sweetness as well as providing fibre, minerals such as potassium, phosphorus and calcium and vitamins.

Light Muscovado sugar - Contains around 6% molasses.

Breads and Crispbreads

Bread has always been considered a staple food in the diet. It is a good source of carbohydrates, low in fat and provides B vitamins and minerals. Select wholemeal breads, rye breads and breads with added seeds as these are especially rich in fibre and essential fatty acids.

Crispbreads are a quick convenient healthy alternative to bread. Ryvita crispbreads are rich in fibre because they are made from whole rye grain, as well as being low in fat, salt and sugar. If you are trying to lose weight just compare the calories, slice for slice, with bread to see how low in calories Ryvita are.

Wholemeal Bread - Made from 100% flour milled from whole grain with nothing removed, so all the nutrients of the grain are still intact.
62 calories per 28g (1oz) slice.

Seeded Pan Gallego - Made from a blend of wheat and wholemeal flours with added pumpkin seeds, sunflower seeds and millet. Made with olive oil. 81 calories per 28g (1oz) slice.

Ryvita Oat Bran Crispbread - Made from wholemeal rye with added Oat Bran. This addition of oat bran increases the dietary fibre content by 20% in comparison to the Original crispbread.
27 calories per slice.

Ryvita Dark Rye Crispbread - Made from 100% wholemeal rye with added malt. This crispbread has a slightly stronger nutty flavour.
25 calories per slice.

Dark Rye Bread - Rye flour gives a dense heavy bread. It is often blended with wheat flour to give a lighter dough. Dark rye bread made from 100% rye has a higher fibre content. It is a low fat bread.
58 calories per 28g (1oz) slice.

Ryvita Original Crispbread - Made from wholemeal rye. It has a light nutty flavour and crunchy texture associated with crispbreads. 25 calories per slice.

Ryvita Sesame Crispbread - Made from wholemeal rye, topped with sesame seeds. It has a slightly lower level of dietary fibre, but still a good source.
33 calories per slice.

Calories, Fat and Fibre Guide

Once you have completed your chosen Zip into Shape Diet you may wish to include some of your own favourite recipes alongside those suggested in the Diet for Life section.

Below is a comprehensive list of basic foods with their calorie, fat and fibre values. Use this information to help you select ingredients for recipes or snacks not included in this book.

For more information on daily recommended calorie, fat and fibre intake see pages 6-7.

Food	Calories (kcal)	Fat (g)	Dietary Fibre (g)
ALMONDS			
shelled, per 28g (1oz)	160	15	4
APPLES			
cooking, flesh only,			
per 28g (1oz)	11	0	0·7
eating, per 28g (1oz)	13	0	0·6
APRICOTS			
dried, per 28g (1oz)	51	0·5	6·7
fresh with stone,			
per 28g (1oz)	8	0	0·5
ARROWROOT			
per 5ml (tsp)	10	0	0

Food	Calories (kcal)	Fat (g)	Dietary Fibre (g)
ASPARAGUS			
per 28g (1oz)	5	0	0·4
AUBERGINES			
per 28g (1oz)	4	0	0·7
AVOCADO			
flesh only, per 28g (1oz)	63	6	0·6
BACON			
per 28g (1oz)			
back bacon, raw	120	11	0
back bacon, well grilled	64	3·5	0
streaky bacon, raw	116	11	0
streaky bacon,			
well grilled	67	3·7	0
BANANA			
flesh only, per 28g (1oz)	22	0·1	1
BEAN SPROUTS			
raw, per 28g (1oz)	8	0	0·3
boiled, per 28g (1oz)	7	0	0·3
BEANS			
per 28g (1oz)			
baked, canned in			
tomato sauce	20	0·1	2
broad, boiled	14	0	1·2
butter, boiled	27	0	1·4
French, boiled	7	0	0·9
red kidney, canned	25	0	2·3
runner, boiled	5	0	0·8
BEEF			
per 28g (1oz)			
braising steak, lean, raw	35	1·5	0
ground, lean, raw	45	1·5	0
minced, raw	74	4	0
rump steak, lean and			
fat, raw	56	3	0
topside, lean, raw	35	1·5	0
BEETROOT			
raw, per 28g (1oz)	8	0	0·9
boiled, per 28g (1oz)	12	0	0·7
BLACKBERRIES			
raw, per 28g (1oz)	8	0	2·1
BLACKCURRANTS			
raw, per 28g (1oz)	8	0	2·4
BRAN			
per 28g (1oz)	58	0·5	12·5
per 15 ml (1 tbsp)	10	0·08	2·1
BRAZIL NUTS			
shelled, per 28g (1oz)	175	16	2·5
BREAD			
per 28g (1oz)			
dark rye	58	0·3	2·1
white	66	0·5	0·5
wholemeal	62	0·8	2·5
BROCCOLI			
raw, per 28g (1oz)	6	0	1
boiled, per 28g (1oz)	5	0	1·1
BUTTER			
per 28g (1oz)	210	23	0

Food	Calories (kcal)	Fat (g)	Dietary Fibre (g)
CABBAGE			
raw, per 28g (1oz)	6	0	0·9
boiled, per 28g (1oz)	4	0	0·8
red, raw per 28g (1oz)	5	0	1
CARROTS			
raw, per 28g (1oz)	6	0	0·8
boiled, per 28g (1oz)	5	0	0·9
CASHEW NUTS			
per 28g (1oz)	160	11	4
CAULIFLOWER			
raw, per 28g (1oz)	4	0	0·6
boiled, per 28g (1oz)	3	0	0·5
CELERY			
raw, per 28g (1oz)	2	0	0·4
boiled, per 28g (1oz)	1	0	0·6
CHEESE			
per 28g (1oz)			
Brie	88	7	0
Camembert	88	7	0
Cheddar	120	9·8	0
Cottage Cheese	27	1·2	0
Diet Cottage Cheese	23	0·5	0
Curd Cheese	54	2·8	0
Dolcellate	100	8	0
Edam	90	7	0
Emmenthal	115	8	0
Feta	85	7	0
Gruyère	117	9·8	0
Mozzarella	90	7·5	0
Parmesan	118	9·8	0
Quark-skimmed milk			
soft cheese	20	0·1	0
Ricotta	55	5·5	0
Roquefort	88	7·5	0
CHERRIES			
fresh, with stones			
per 28g (1oz)	12	0	0·4
CHESTNUTS			
shelled, per 28g (1oz)	48	7	1·9
CHICKEN			
per 28g (1oz)			
meat only, raw	34	1·5	0
on the bone, no skin, raw	25	0·7	0
CHICK PEAS			
cooked, per 28g (1oz)	40	3·4	6·7
CHICORY			
raw, per 28g (1oz)	3	0	0·4
CHINESE LEAVES			
raw, per 28g (1oz)	3	0	0·6

Food	Calories (kcal)	Fat (g)	Dietary Fibre (g)
CHOCOLATE			
per 28g (1oz)			
milk or plain	150	4	0
COCONUT			
desiccated, per 28g (1oz)	171	17	6·6
fresh, per 28g (1oz)	100	10	3·8
fresh coconut milk,			
per 28 ml (1 floz)	6	0	0
COD			
fillet, raw per 28g (1oz)	22	0	0
on the bone, raw,			
per 28g (1oz)	15	0	0
COFFEE			
beans, roasted and			
ground infusion	0	0	0
instant, per 5 ml (tsp)	0	0	0
COLEY			
raw, per 28g (1oz)	21	0	0
CORNED BEEF			
per 28g (1oz)	62	2·8	0
CORNFLOUR			
per 28g (1oz)	100	0	0·8
per 15 ml (tbsp)	33	0	0·3
COURGETTES			
raw, per 28g (1oz)	4	0	0·5
CRAB			
meat only, per 28g (1oz)	36	1·5	0
CRISPBREADS			
per slice			
Ryvita Dark Rye	25	0·2	1·3
Ryvita Oat Bran	27	0·26	1·9
Ryvita Original	25	0·2	1·3
Ryvita Sesame	33	0·66	1·1
CREAM			
per 28g (1oz)			
crème fraîche	106	11·2	0
double	125	13·4	0
single	53	5	0
soured	60	5·9	0
CUCUMBER			
per 28g (1oz)	3	0	0·1
CURRANTS			
per 28g (1oz)	69	3	2·2
DATES			
dried, stoned			
per 28g (1oz)	70	1·5	2·4
dried, with stones			
per 28g (1oz)	60	1·4	2·1
fresh, with stones			
per 28g (1oz)	30	0	0·8
DUCK			
per 28g (1oz)			
raw, meat only	35	1·5	0
raw, meat, fat and skin	122	4·2	0
roast, meat only	54	3	0

Food	Calories (kcal)	Fat (g)	Dietary Fibre (g)
EGGS, each			
Size 1	95	7	0
Size 2	90	6·5	0
Size 3	80	5·5	0
Size 4	75	5	0
yolk, size 3	65	5·5	0
white, size 3	15	0	0
ENDIVE			
raw, per 28g (1oz)	3	0	0·6
FIGS			
dried, per 28g (1oz)	60	1·5	5·2
fresh, per 28g (1oz)	12	0	1·7
FLOUR			
rye, per 28g (1oz)	95	0·7	3·3
white, plain per 28g (1oz)	99	0	1·5
white, self raising			
per 28g (1oz)	96	0	1
wholemeal, per 28g (1oz)	90	0·7	2·7
white, per 15 ml (tbsp)	32	0	0·3
wholemeal, per 15 ml (tbsp)	29	0·2	0·9
FRENCH DRESSING			
per 15 ml (tbsp)	75	8·5	0
oil-free, per 15 ml (tbsp)	5	0	0
GARLIC			
1 clove	0	0	0
GELATINE			
powdered, per 15 ml (tbsp)	30	0	0
GOOSEBERRIES			
ripe, dessert, per 28g (1oz)	10	0	1
cooking, per 28g (1oz)	5	0	0·9
GRAPEFRUIT			
flesh and skin, per 28g (1oz)	3	0	0·1
flesh only, per 28g (1oz)	6	0	0·2
juice, per 28 ml (1 floz)	9	0	0
GRAPES			
black, per 28g (1oz)	14	0	0·1
white, per 28g (1oz)	17	0	0·25
GREENGAGES			
fresh, with stones,			
per 28g (1oz)	13	0	0·7
HADDOCK			
per 28g (1oz)			
fillet, raw	21	0	0
on the bone, raw	15	0	0
smoked fillet, raw	25	0	0
HALIBUT			
on the bone, raw,			
per 28g (1oz)	26	0	0
HAM			
boiled, lean per 28g (1oz)	47	1·5	0
HAZELNUTS			
shelled, per 28g (1oz)	108	10	1·7
HERRING			
fillet, raw per 28g (1oz)	66	5·5	0

Food	Calories (kcal)	Fat (g)	Dietary Fibre (g)
HONEY			
per 15 ml (tbsp)	60	0·7	0
JAM			
per 15 ml (tbsp)	45	0·7	0·2
KIDNEY			
raw, per 28g (1oz)	25	0·7	0
LAMB			
per 28g (1oz)			
leg, raw, boneless,			
lean and fat	68	5·5	0
leg, roast, boneless,			
lean and fat	75	5·5	0
leg, roast, boneless,			
lean only	54	3	0
LEEKS			
raw, per 28g (1oz)	9	0	0·8
LEMON			
flesh and skin,			
per 28g (1oz)	4	0	1·5
juice, per 5 ml (tsp)	0	0	0
LENTILS			
raw, per 28g (1oz)	85	0	3·3
split, boiled, per 28g (1oz)	28	0	1
LETTUCE			
per 28g (1oz)	3	0	0·4
LIVER			
per 28g (1oz)			
calves', raw	43	2·5	0
chickens', raw	38	1·5	0
lambs', raw	51	3	0
MACARONI			
white, raw, per 28g (1oz)	105	0·7	0·8
wholewheat, raw			
per 28g (1oz)	95	0·7	2·8
white, boiled			
per 28g (1oz)	33	0	0·3
wholewheat, boiled			
per 28g (1oz)	30	0	0·9
MACKEREL			
per 28g (1oz)			
fillet, raw	63	4	0
smoked fillet	70	7	0
MANGO			
raw, per 28g (1oz)	17	0	0·4
MARGARINE			
per 28g (1oz)	210	22	0
MARROW			
raw, per 28g (1oz)	5	0	0·5
boiled, per 28g (1oz)	2	0	0·2

Food	Calories (kcal)	Fat (g)	Dietary Fibre (g)	Food	Calories (kcal)	Fat (g)	Dietary Fibre (g)
MELON				PEACH			
per 28g (1oz)				per 28g (1oz)			
cantaloupe, with skin	4	0	0·1	canned in natural juice	13	0	0·2
honeydew, with skin	4	0	0·1	canned in syrup	25	0·7	0·2
ogen, with skin	5	0	0·2	fresh with stone	9	0	0·3
MILK				PEANUTS			
per 284 ml (½ pt)				per 28g (1oz)			
buttermilk	115	0·3	0	roasted and salted	162	14	2·3
pasteurized	190	11	0	shelled	162	14	2·3
semi-skimmed	135	4·8	0	peanut butter	177	15	2·1
skimmed	100	0·2	0	PEARS			
MONKFISH				dessert, raw			
steamed, per 28g (1oz)	28	0·3	0	per 28g (1oz)	8	0	0·5
MUSHROOMS				PEAS			
raw, per 28g (1oz)	4	0	0·7	per 28g (1oz)			
MUSSELS				fresh, boiled	15	0	1·5
shelled, boiled				frozen, boiled	12	0	2·2
per 28g (1oz)	25	0·7	0	split, raw	88	0	3·4
MUSTARD & CRESS				PEPPERS			
per 28g (1oz)	3	0	1	red or green,			
				per 28g (1oz)	4	0	0·3
NECTARINE				yellow, per 28g (1oz)	10	0	0·3
raw, per 28g (1oz)	14	0	0·7	PILCHARDS			
				canned in tomato sauce,			
OATMEAL				per 28g (1oz)	36	1·5	0
raw, per 28g (1oz)	114	3	2	PIMENTOS			
OIL				canned in brine,			
corn, olive, sunflower,				per 28g (1oz)	6	0	0·2
vegetable, per 28 ml				PINEAPPLES			
(1 floz)	255	28	0	per 28g (1oz)			
all varieties, per 15 ml				canned in natural juice	15	0	0·2
(tbsp)	120	13	0	canned in syrup	22	0·7	0·2
OLIVES				fresh, without skin	13	0	0·3
stoned, in brine,				PLAICE			
per 28g (1oz)	29	3	1·2	fillet, raw per 28g (1oz)	26	0·7	0
ONIONS				PLUMS			
raw, per 28g (1oz)	7	0	0·4	per 28g (1oz)			
boiled, per 28g (1oz)	4	0	0·3	cooking, with stones	6	0	0·6
ORANGE				dessert, with stones	10	0	0·6
flesh, per 28g (1oz)	10	0	0·6	PORK			
flesh and skin,				per 28g (1oz)			
per 28g (1oz)	7	0	0·4	fillet, raw	42	3	0
juice, per 28 ml (1 floz)	11	0	0	leg, raw, lean only,			
				boneless	42	3	0
PARSNIP				POTATOES			
raw, per 28g (1oz)	14	0	1·1	per 28g (1oz)			
boiled, per 28g (1oz)	16	0	0·7	old, baked with skin	24	0	0·7
PASTA				old, boiled	23	0	0·3
white, raw, per 28g (1oz)	105	0	0·8	new, boiled	22	0	0·5
white, boiled, per 28g (1oz)	33	0	0·3	PRAWNS			
wholewheat, raw,				shelled, per 28g (1oz)	30	0·7	0
per 28g (1oz)	95	0·7	2·8	PRUNES			
wholewheat, boiled,				dried, stoned per			
				28g (1oz)	46	1·5	4·6
				RADISH			
				per 28g (1oz)	4	0	0·5

Food	Calories (kcal)	Fat (g)	Dietary Fibre (g)	Food	Calories (kcal)	Fat (g)	Dietary Fibre (g)
RAISIN				TANGERINES			
per 28g (1oz)	70	3	2·8	per 28g (1oz)			
RASPBERRIES				flesh only	10	0	0·5
per 28g (1oz)	7	0	2·1	flesh and skin	7	0	1·8
REDCURRANTS				TEA			
per 28g (1oz)	6	0	2·3	all brands, per cup,			
RHUBARB				no milk	0	0	0
raw, per 28g (1oz)	2	0	0·7	TOMATOES			
RICE				per 28g (1oz)			
per 28g (1oz)				canned	3	0	0·2
brown ,raw	99	0·7	1·2	raw	4	0	0·4
white, raw	102	0	0·3	purée	19	0	0
brown, boiled	33	0	0·4	TREACLE			
white, boiled	35	0	0·1	per 15 ml (tbsp)	50	1·5	0
				TROUT			
SALAD CREAM				per 28g (1oz)			
per 15 ml (tbsp)	50	4	0	fillet, smoked	38	1·5	0
SALMON				trout, whole, poached	25	1	0
per 28g (1oz)				TUNA			
canned	44	3	0	per 28g (1oz)			
fresh, raw, flesh only	52	3	0	canned in brine	30	0	0
SARDINES				canned in oil	82	5·5	0
per 28g (1oz)				TURKEY			
canned in oil, drained	62	4·2	0	per 28g (1oz)			
canned in tomato sauce	50	2·8	0	meat only, raw	30	0·7	0
SAUSAGES				meat only, roast	40	0·7	0
per 28g (1oz)				TURNIPS			
beef	25	2	0	raw, per 28g (1oz)	6	0	0·8
pork	33	2·8	0	boiled, per 28g (1oz)	4	0	0·6
pork and beef	30	2·3	0				
SHRIMPS				VEAL			
per 28g (1oz)				fillet, raw per 28g (1oz)	31	0·7	0
canned	27	0	0	VENISON			
fresh, shelled	11	0	0	roast, per 28g (1oz)	56	1·4	0
SMETANA				VINEGAR			
per 28g (1oz)	36	2·8	0	per 28 ml (1 floz)	1	0	0
SOLE							
per 28g (1oz)				WALNUTS			
fillet, raw	23	0	0	shelled, per 28g (1oz)	149	14	1·5
fillet, steamed	26	0	0	WATERCRESS			
SPINACH				per 28g (1oz)	4	0	0·9
boiled, per 28g (1oz)	9	0	1·7	WATERMELON			
SPRING GREENS				per 28g (1oz)			
boiled, per 28g (1oz)	3	0	1·1	flesh only	6	0	0·2
SPRING ONIONS				flesh and skin	3	0	0·1
raw, per 28g (1oz)	10	0	0·4	WHEATGERM			
STRAWBERRIES				per 15 ml (tbsp)	18	0·4	0·1
fresh or frozen,				WORCESTERSHIRE			
per 28g (1oz)	7	0	0·6	SAUCE			
SUGAR				per 15 ml (tbsp)	13	0	0
per 28g (1oz)	112	2·8	0				
SULTANAS				YOGURT			
per 28g (1oz)	71	1·5	1·9	per 28g (1oz)			
SWEETCORN				low fat natural	14	0·2	0
per 28g (1oz)				strained Greek style	36	2·8	0
canned in brine	22	0	1·6				
fresh kernels only, boiled	25	0	1·3				

Index

Index